A TANGLE OF NURSES

A TANGLE OF NURSES

Lynne Collins

Chivers Press • Thorndike Press
Bath, England • Thorndike, Maine USA

This Large Print edition is published by Chivers Press, England, and by Thorndike Press, USA.

Published in 1998 in the U.K. by arrangement with the author's agent.

Published in 1998 in the U.S. by arrangement with Laurence Pollinger, Ltd.

U.K. Hardcover ISBN 0–7540–3112–8 (Chivers Large Print)
U.S. Softcover   ISBN 0–7862–1226–8 (General Series Edition)

The characters in this story are entirely fictitious and no reference to any living persons is implied.

The text of this Large Print edition is unabridged.
Other aspects of the book may vary from the original edition.

Set in 16 pt. New Times Roman.

Printed in Great Britain on acid-free paper.

British Library Cataloguing in Publication Data available

Library of Congress Cataloging-in-Publication Data

Collins, Lynne.
  A tangle of nurses / Lynne Collins.
    p.   cm.
  ISBN 0–7862–1226–8 (large print : sc : alk. paper)
  1. Large type books.   I. Title.
[PS3553.O47494T36   1998]
813'.54—dc21

                                                                    97–29673

CHAPTER ONE

Janet was grateful for her brother's company as she waited for the London train. Her holiday with her family had been all-too-brief and, much as she looked forward to the second year of her training at St. Cecilia's, it was a wrench to leave her happy, friendly home. Gil had voluntarily taken the morning off to take her to the station and see her safely on to the train—and Janet felt that he sensed and appreciated her feelings. Anstey Moor, a small country town near the Cumberland coast, was many miles from London and so she was only able to return home two or three times in a year. There were times when she envied those girls who lived in or near London and could visit their families on free days and weekends.

She was young and full of a zest for life that had its own appeal. Soft, fair hair rioted in a tumbled mass of curls about her small head and her grey eyes held a natural candour. Brother and sister were very alike. Gil was tall and lean and his fair hair was sleeked smoothly back from his brow but the merry grey eyes that played havoc with the female population of Anstey Moor held the same, pleasing candour in their depths.

He gave Janet a cigarette and flicked his lighter into life. 'Nice to have had you home,' he said with warm sincerity. 'Mum worries about you, Jan—until she sees how well you look and can find out for herself that you're really happy at St. Cecilia's.'

'I love it,' she said swiftly. 'I wish it was a local hospital,' she added with a sigh. 'London is such a heck of a journey from home.' She studied the glowing end of her cigarette. 'Mum always worries even when there isn't any need.'

He nodded. 'She's not too happy about this chap you're going about with,' he said frankly.

'Dominic?' Faint colour stole into her cheeks.

'But I've told her all about him.'

'He's a lot older than you, isn't he?'

'Fourteen years ... it is quite a difference, I suppose. But I never notice it, honestly. He's very good to me, Gil.'

'You were aiming high, though, weren't you? A surgeon ... isn't there some rule in hospitals about junior nurses not fraternising with senior staff?'

Janet shrugged. 'It is rather frowned on ... but there isn't much anyone can do as long as we behave with discretion in the hospital precincts. Don't talk as though Dominic and I were having an affair ... we're only friends.' But the colour was still high in her cheeks.

He grinned. 'You're pretty fond of him, Jan.' It was not a question.

She nodded. 'Yes, I am.' She tilted her chin in a gesture that was almost defiant. 'I may even marry him—if he asks me!'

He whistled softly. 'What about your training? I thought you were so keen on nursing.'

'I am. I don't mean marry him right away—when I've finished training. But I don't even know that he'll want to marry me,' she ended abruptly.

'Tell me about him,' he invited.

'Oh ... he's very attractive and very clever. He has a lovely house and he lives on his own except for a cook-housekeeper. He's the Senior Surgical Officer at St. Cecilia's ... and he's a friend of Helen's family.'

'Is that how you met him ... through Helen?' She was silent a moment, remembering their first meeting on Thomas Chalmers Ward ... her humiliation and distress because of an accident with a locker and his own dry, humorous charm that had immediately dried the threatened tears. 'No ... we met on one of the wards. But we didn't become friends until some weeks later ... when he invited me to go with him to the Commemoration Ball. Until then I believed he was virtually engaged to Helen.' Her voice fell a little on the last words. She preferred to forget the heartache and misery of those weeks when she had been convinced that Dominic and her friend were in love and intended to marry. She had not blamed him for loving the beautiful, sophisticated Helen—and she had not really

3

expected her love for him to evoke any response in a man who was almost a stranger. The hospital grapevine was to blame for the rumour that Dominic Hammond was engaged to Helen Wilmot, the daughter of the famous heart specialist, Sir Henry Wilmot. It had been an incredible relief to learn that Helen did not care for Dominic and that she was in love with a playwright to whom she was now engaged.

She had missed Dominic during the past fortnight for she was used to spending a great deal of her spare time in his company. He had written to her and admitted that he was impatient for her return to London ... surely that was evidence that he loved her, would want to marry her one day in the misty future?

'I must meet this Helen one day,' Gil said lightly, breaking into her thoughts. 'She sounds just my type.'

'She's engaged to Adrian Hart ... the man who wrote *Aurora* and *Darkest Dawn*.'

'Anyone can make a mistake,' he said blithely.

Janet laughed. 'She's very nice ... you'd like her, Gil.' She and Helen had been friends since her first day at St. Cecilia's when they had found themselves sharing a room—together with Sally Calvert. The three girls had become fast friends although they were very different types from very different backgrounds.

Helen's father was a famous heart specialist: her mother was a famous actress, Greta

4

Beaumont. She had chosen to nurse as a relief from the boredom and emptiness of the social whirl which had been her life since she returned from a finishing school in Switzerland. Her father had encouraged her decision: her mother had openly disapproved; her friends had warned Helen that the work was rigorous and distasteful. No one believed that she would continue with her training once the first enthusiasm had waned. But Helen promised to be an excellent nurse—if she did not marry Adrian Hart before she could finish her training. She was certainly engaged to him but her plans for the future were very vague.

Sally was the daughter of elderly parents who had never expected her to nurse. She had been planning the final details of her wedding when her fiancé broke their engagement on the plea that he was in love with her closest friend. The pain and disappointment, the humiliating sympathy of friends and neighbours, had determined Sally to try a new way of life, to escape from people and surroundings that provided constant reminders of a former happiness. Her life had revolved around Roger Gale since her schooldays ... it had not been easy to adjust to a way of life without him. She had taken up nursing on an impulse and had been on the verge of throwing it up during the first months. But now, nursing was important to her and it seemed that she had managed to forget the old heartache.

Janet was fond of her two friends. In the past year, she had come to know them both very well. They had studied together, helped each other, encouraged each other, enjoyed their leisure hours together in cinema, theatre, coffee bar or at parties. They were a popular trio and much of their popularity stemmed from their light-hearted approach to the opposite sex. Very few of the students could afford to become emotionally involved with a junior nurse ... and there was safety in numbers.

'We've always liked the same people,' he agreed easily. 'But I'm not sure about this Dominic Hammond, you know. I hope he isn't leading you up the garden path, Jan.'

Anger sparked in her grey eyes. 'Why should he? He doesn't need to waste his time on a junior nurse! He must know dozens of women ... all far more attractive and more sophisticated than I am! He's fond of me, Gil!'

He smiled at her affectionately. 'Can't say that I blame him ... he'll be a lucky chap if you do marry him.'

She gave him a little, half-laughing push, her anger forgotten. 'Oh, you're biased!'

'You've talked about him a lot while you've been home,' he said thoughtfully. 'I guess you're pretty fond of him ... but somehow he doesn't seem your type from all I've heard.'

'You don't know him,' she said decisively.

'True ... and perhaps that's what seems

6

wrong. If he wants to marry you why didn't he come home with you and meet your family?'

'Don't be silly, Gil! He's a busy man ... he just can't leave the hospital and his private work to come all this way. After all, we're not engaged ... or anything,' she finished with a trace of dejection in her voice.

'What happened to that other chap ... Martin something or other?'

'Martin Grey? Oh, I still see him occasionally.' She glanced at him swiftly. 'That was a very platonic affair ... I didn't break his heart when I started going out with Dominic, you know.'

Martin Grey had once been Janet's constant companion and escort. He was one of the housemen, an attractive and flirtatious young man. Janet liked him because he reminded her very much of Gil ... and that was exactly how she had always thought of Martin—as another brother. She was well aware that his regard for her was not tinged with romance and it was pleasant to have a friend like Martin, someone she could always rely on, talk to as easily as though he were Gil and always be assured of his interest, his understanding and his affection.

There was a faint stirring of movement along the platform. Passengers began to gather the bits and pieces of their luggage, to collect straying children, to make their farewells of those who were not boarding the approaching train.

'You're sure you've got everything?' Gil demanded, familiar with his sister's flair for losing or forgetting something vital at the last minute.

Janet checked that her ticket was safely in her bag, that her gloves were in the pocket of her coat, that her gay scarf was tucked about her neck and that she had the small telescopic umbrella fastened to her wrist. Gil found her an empty compartment and hoisted her bulging case on to the rack.

'Well ... be seeing you, Jan,' he said cheerfully and submitted to a sisterly kiss on the cheek before stepping back and ensuring that the door was securely closed.

Jan stood at the door and waved until her arm ached and Gil was a mere speck on a distant station platform.

Then she sighed and sank into her seat, thinking of the long journey ahead of her with a faint grimace touching her mouth. It was like Gil, dear soul that he was, to see her off. Her father was a busy G.P. and he would be dealing with a heavy surgery at this hour. Her mother would be bustling about the busy market and then preparing a substantial lunch which her husband might or might not have time to enjoy. Danny, of course, would be at school.

Her grey eyes held a warm smile as she thought of the family she loved so much. They were a happy, united family—and this time the wrench of leaving them seemed greater. Perhaps because her mother was at last coming to the point of talking to her as though she was an adult instead of an irrepressible little girl ... or because her father was so deeply interested in all she had to tell him of St. Cecilia's and her work on the wards ... or perhaps because Gil's newest romance seemed as though it might be the real thing at last ... or perhaps because Danny was growing up into a more responsible boy and was less prone to practical jokes and tactless teasing.

Her thoughts inevitably turned to Dominic—and what he would think of her family when he met them ... as meet them he must if they ever did decide to get married. Now, more than ever, she was conscious of the great gulf in their backgrounds. Dominic's family had always been wealthy and well-bred: he was the product of public school and university and medical school; he had moved in sophisticated social circles. Janet stood just a little in awe of Dominic—and despised herself for doing so.

She loved him, of course ... but it was strange that she could seldom feel really at ease with him and there was no swift, mutual affinity between them that she had known with Martin, for instance. She could never really forget that he was a man of brilliant standing and success, that he was wealthy and sophisticated, that he was older and more

9

experienced in the ways of the world, that he was on a far higher level than herself in the profession they shared. Not that Dominic was ever guilty of emphasising these differences. Yet she was always conscious that something stood between them ... and sometimes she wondered if it was the shadow of Helen.

Helen had once admitted that Dominic had proposed to her and she had refused him. It was only logical to assume that he had loved Helen—and Janet could not help wondering if he still did so. They had a great deal in common and they were friends of long standing. So it was all the more surprising that he seemed indifferent to her engagement to Adrian Hart—and apparently preferred a girl who could not hold a candle to Helen for looks, charm, personality and eligibility.

Janet had met with a great deal of teasing because of her friendship with Dominic Hammond but she had grown up with two mischievous brothers and was inured to teasing. She was willing to admit that it was an odd friendship ... in her heart, she frequently doubted that Dominic loved her and would want to marry her. She could only hope that in time he would forget Helen and grow to love her as much as she loved him...

She was so lost in thought that she scarcely heard the sound of the sliding door which led to the compartment. A tall, broad-shouldered man entered the compartment and sat down in

10

the opposite corner. A brief-case slid to the floor as he did so ... and the slap of leather startled Janet.

Their eyes met across the compartment and he smiled ruefully. Janet did not realise the bewilderment of her expression.

'I hope I'm not disturbing you,' he said quietly.

'Oh ... no, of course not,' she said hastily. She smiled—and then looked away before she could observe the sparking of interest in his dark eyes. Janet was much too modest to appreciate the shattering impression that her lovely smile could have upon a stranger.

He took a sheaf of galley-proofs from his brief-case, uncapped a fountain pen and tried to concentrate on the printed words. But he was annoyingly conscious of the slim and remarkably pretty girl in the opposite corner and his glance slid frequently towards her. He admired her easy self-possession and was thankful that she was not one of those silly chits who imagined that if a man spoke, however briefly he was prepared to pass a dull journey in meaningless flirtation. She seemed to have forgotten him, her gaze on the passing countryside, so absorbed in her own thoughts that he found himself wondering what occupied her mind so intently.

Again he bent over the galley-proofs and was soon busy with the necessary corrections. He hated long journeys, hated trains ... would not be on this train if his own car had been available ... and it had seemed a good idea to provide himself with something that demanded concentration to while away the hours.

Janet rose to her feet and reached for her case. She had packed a book of crosswords to solve on the train ... a favourite occupation and one that could certainly help the hours to pass quickly. It was difficult to balance herself in the swaying train as it rounded a sharp curve and she was not tall enough to reach easily to the rack.

He watched her absently, his thoughts still with his proofs—and then he thrust them aside and leaped to his feet, cursing his slowness to realise her difficulty.

'May I help you?'

She turned to him gratefully. 'Would you mind?'

With ease he lifted the case from the rack and set it on the seat. 'There you are!'

'Thank you so much. My brother always forgets that not everyone has his quota of inches ... I usually put my case on the seat if the compartment isn't full,' she explained.

He looked down at her, smiling. Certainly she was not very tall ... five foot one or two, he imagined, and, unlike many girls, she did not wear high heels to give her extra inches.

'So that tall young man was your brother ... I thought the resemblance was rather marked,'

12

he said lightly.

Surprise touched her eyes. 'Oh ... did you see us?' Sudden suspicion gleamed in the depths of her grey eyes. She suddenly realised for the first time that he had entered the compartment some minutes after the train had left Anstey Moor—and she wondered apprehensively if he had deliberately sought her out.

'I boarded the train at Anstey Moor,' he explained. 'You were standing a few feet away from me on the platform.' Abruptly he understood the wariness of her gaze. 'I fell foul of a woman with a yapping pekinese and a mother with two noisy children ... so I thought I'd better change my compartment if I wanted to get any work done.' He indicated the galley-proofs and stooped to pick up a couple that had slipped to the floor.

His smile was so open, his eyes so frank, his tone so reassuring that Janet's understandable apprehension was swept away.

He sat down with every indication of relapsing into silence and returning to his work ... and Janet opened her case and took out her book of crosswords. Then she realised that she had forgotten to bring pen or pencil with her—and she uttered an involuntary exclamation of dismay.

Her travelling companion looked up swiftly, glanced at the cover of her book and at her dismayed face and his swift intuition supplied

13

the reason for that exclamation. He took a pencil from his breast pocket and leaned forward.

'Would you care to borrow this?'

'That's very kind of you ... how did you know?'

He smiled. 'It was just a lucky guess.' She took the silver propelling pencil with a word of thanks. 'You enjoy those things?' he asked lightly. 'I'm hopeless at solving crosswords.'

'These are very easy,' she said. 'I'm not very good but I enjoy trying to solve them.'

'I imagine that it's a more amusing pastime than this kind of thing.' And he tapped the galley-proofs with a rueful smile touching his lips.

'What are they?' she asked curiously.

'Proofs ... haven't you seen any before?' He passed over a handful of the long, flimsy sheets. Janet studied them, a faint frown creasing her brow.

'Proofs for a book,' he enlightened her.

'Oh, I see. Do you work for a publishing firm?'

He laughed with genuine amusement. 'I suppose you could say so!'

'That must be very interesting work.'

'Not this part of it,' he assured her with a mock grimace. 'It's an extremely boring task, believe me.' He took pity on her evident bewilderment. 'I wrote the darn stuff and checking the proofs merely convinces me that I

14

should have consigned the manuscript to the fire. Now it's too late ... and within a few weeks an unsuspecting public will pay good money to read this rubbish.'

Janet studied him with interest. 'You're a writer!'

'Of sorts.'

'And you really manage to sell your books?'

'From time to time,' he told her, his eyes dancing.

'How nice to get paid for something that you enjoy,' she said naively.

'Yes, I agree with you ... writing is a reasonably lucrative way of using up one's spare time,' he said with faint sarcasm.

Janet flushed slightly. 'I didn't mean to imply that writing was just a hobby.'

'Of course you didn't,' he agreed reassuringly. He smiled at her with friendliness in his eyes. 'You seem envious ... do you get paid for something that you don't enjoy?'

'I'm a nurse ... and I love it,' she told him firmly.

He thought her refreshing ... a straightforward and appealing girl. There had been few such women in his life ... It was his experience that most women were devious, cunning and determined and he thought it to his credit that he had managed to escape their designs so far.

Janet rather liked the look of him. He was

not strictly good-looking but his dark eyes were attractive and reassuring and she liked the way that amusement quirked the corners of his mouth. He was a mature, personable man with intelligent features, a firm chin that hinted at obstinacy or determination, thick black hair that grew low in curling tendrils on the nape of his neck.

They were strangers ... and would remain so, of course. Ships that passed in the night. Yet there was no harm in whiling away the journey in conversation with this friendly man ... and she was very curious to know more about him.

CHAPTER TWO

'Where do you nurse?' he asked.

'St. Cecilia's ... do you know it? It's in London.'

He smiled. 'I know *of* it. I've never had much to do with hospitals, fortunately. Are they anything like the popular fiction of the moment?'

'In what way?'

His eyes teased her gently. 'Oh, intrigues in the linen cupboard ... innocent nurses warding off the amorous pursuit of doctors ... patients falling in love with the pretty angel of mercy.'

'Romance is usually the last thing to be found on a hospital ward,' Janet assured him firmly.

He glanced at her hands. Her ring finger was bare and he wondered if such an attractive girl was really unattached. Perhaps she was dedicated to nursing—or perhaps the man in her life had not yet come to the point—or perhaps she preferred to share her favours among a number of young men.

Janet noticed that swift glance and understood its implication. Faint colour stole into her cheeks.

He said drily: 'Are the young men of today so indifferent to pretty nurses—or are the nurses too devoted to their work?'

'Hospital sisters are much too eagle-eyed,' she retorted lightly.

'You're not working every minute of the day—and hospital sisters don't lurk in corners when you're off duty with your friends, surely?'

'Nursing is a demanding life ... and one doesn't have much time or inclination for dates.' Oddly she felt very much at ease with this stranger ... they were talking as easily as though they were old friends. She did not resent the implication of his questions ... she was faintly amused that he should be so interested in her ringless hand.

'You seem to be missing a great deal!'

Janet laughed. 'Love laughs at rules and regulations, you know. St. Cecilia's has its fair share of romances. As a matter of fact, one of my friends is engaged to an ex-patient ...

although they did know each other before he was admitted. A nurse risks her job if she gets involved with a patient—and she has to be careful if she has an affair with a doctor or a houseman.'

'And you?' he asked lightly. 'Heartwhole and fancy-free?'

'Me? Oh, I'm not engaged or ... or anything.'

She wondered at her evasion. Certainly it was none of his business but she did not resent his interest. It would have been easy to make a flippant retort or even to mention that she hoped to be engaged in the near future. Instead, she had sheered away from the reminder of Dominic and hastened to assure a complete stranger that she had no emotional complications. She told herself that she was so unsure of Dominic's feelings that she would not tempt fate by talking even to a stranger of their lukewarm affair.

It was amazing how quickly that long journey passed. His galley-proofs lay neglected on the seat and before long the two heads, dark and fair, were bowed over Janet's book of crossword puzzles. They might have known each other for years—and the compartment resounded with their eager voices and lively laughter. They had lunch together in the dining-car ... and he wisely did not insist on paying for her meal. Janet told him about her family and her home: he explained that he had been staying on the outskirts of Anstey Moor, gathering copy for a new book and picking up the threads of an old friendship; they discussed books and music and films and theatre—and touched lightly on almost every subject under the sun.

Janet felt that it was a pity that it was just one of those brief encounters, that she would never see him again once they said their farewells at Paddington. How nice he was, charming and easy to like, how utterly reliable and trustworthy he had proved himself to be in circumstances where another man might well have taken advantage of the long, dull journey to enter into a reckless, short-lived flirtation.

She went to powder her nose as familiar landmarks indicated that they would reach Paddington very shortly. When she returned, he was straightening his tie before the compartment mirror and her case was resting on the seat. He had returned his galley-proofs to the briefcase and the abrupt tidiness of the compartment seemed an unwelcome reminder that they would soon be taking leave of each other. Janet felt a wave of shyness as he turned to smile and make way for her to pass him.

A shadow fell across the compartment and a ticket collector drew back the door. 'Tickets, please!'

Eden brought out his wallet and handed over his ticket. Janet searched her handbag ... but there was no trace of the small piece of green pasteboard. Flushed and confused, she turned out the contents of her bag—but the ticket had disappeared. The man waited with dour patience ... his whole attitude implying that he was used to silly women who mislaid their tickets and were in the habit of looking half a dozen times in the right place without seeing what was under their noses.

Janet hunted through her coat pockets, searched the contents of her bag once more— all in vain. Dismayed and embarrassed, she turned to the waiting ticket collector.

'I did have it ... I can't think how I've lost it.'

'Lost it, have you, miss?' His voice held weary resignation.

'I suppose so ... I must have,' she said helplessly.

'Well, you'll have to pay the fare, miss—then if the ticket is found and handed in you'll be refunded in due course.'

She stared at him, knowing she did not have enough in her purse to pay the expensive single fare from Anstey Moor to Paddington.

Eden produced his wallet. 'How much?'

'I don't know where the lady's come from,' the man pointed out, reasonably enough.

'Anstey Moor.'

Janet turned to the man who had been such a pleasant travelling companion. 'But I can't let you pay....'

The ticket collector thumbed through a small book, announced the fare and accepted the notes which were pushed into his hand. 'The lady's name and address, if you don't mind, sir.'

Janet supplied the details as the train slowed down to enter the big terminus. The ticket collector departed with a further assurance that her money would be refunded if the original ticket was found.

'Your money, he means,' Janet said ruefully. 'I don't suppose it will ever turn up. How careless of me! I know I had the ticket when I got on the train.'

'It's very annoying,' he agreed. 'But don't worry about it now ... the matter is settled.'

'I shouldn't have allowed you to pay....'

He smiled down at her warmly. 'Helping damsels in distress is a hobby of mine.'

He helped her down to the platform with a firm hand beneath her elbow. Flustered by the incident, colour was high in her cheeks and she looked extremely pretty and very youthful. Because he held her case, she had no choice but to walk beside him towards the barrier—and she had no reason to object. No one could have been nicer or kinder or more helpful than this stranger—she must find out his name and address in order to repay him.

As they mingled with the crowd, he suggested that they should have some tea in the buffet. Janet was amazed by the abrupt feeling of relief that they were not to part immediately. They talked for some time and Eden was equally conscious of a reluctance to part from this attractive girl without some arrangement for a future meeting.

Janet said impulsively: 'I don't even know your name!'

He smiled. 'An oversight on my part. It's Eden ... Eden Varndell. It scarcely seems possible that we've been together for six hours without exchanging names.'

'I'm Janet Finlay.'

He nodded. 'I know—you gave your name and address to the ticket collector—remember?' He was faintly amused that his name had meant nothing to her for he was a successful writer and his latest book was a best-seller ... articles about him had appeared in magazines, he had been interviewed by the national press and on television, his book was on sale in almost every bookshop in England—and yet Janet Finlay had apparently never heard of him. It was rather refreshing and he was pleased that she did not pretend to know his name or to have read his books.

'We talked about everything but ourselves,' she reminded him. Then, a soft blush surging into her face, she added: 'At least, you did ... I seem to have told you a lot about myself.'

'Oh, I'm a good listener,' he said, his eyes bright with laughter. 'I really enjoyed the journey, you know. You've told me so much about hospital life that I'm tempted to throw up writing and take up medicine immediately.'

Janet threw him a laughing glance through the thick veil of her lashes. 'Come to St. Cecilia's then!'

At last, reluctantly, Janet rose to her feet. It was over an hour since they had arrived at Paddington and she might be keeping him from his own affairs. They left the buffet and then Janet hesitated, at a loss, knowing how likely it was that he would simply walk away and she would never see him again.

'A taxi?' he suggested.

'Public transport,' she amended, laughing.

'I have to go your way,' he told her disarmingly. 'Why not share my taxi ... I expect you've had enough of trains for one day.'

'Are you sure it won't take you out of your way?' she demurred yet knowing that she welcomed his suggestion.

'Not in the least. I feel responsible for your safety, anyway ... London is a dangerous place for country girls on their own.'

'I've had a year to find my feet in London!'

'Don't destroy my illusions. I'm convinced that you'll get lost or run over by a bus unless I deliver you safely to St. Cecilia's.'

She sat beside him in the taxi, listening to his light conversation, conscious of his nearness and the unsteady, bewildering thud of her heart. She would not have thought it possible for any man other than Dominic to quicken her pulses. She chided her foolish heart ... he had been kind and friendly, his interest was merely passing and unimportant, he would forget her once they parted and although she might think of him from time to time, remembering his kindness, his charm, his warm personality, eventually she would find it difficult to recall his name or anything else about him. It was merely a brief encounter that was exciting while it lasted but which could never develop into anything more disturbing.

This very evening, she would be with Dominic again. She had promised to telephone to arrange a meeting ... and once she was with him the strange magic of this man's personality would have no power to disturb. She would be back on the wards the next day and be much too busy to indulge in day-dreams about a stranger she had met on a train.

What did she know of him, after all? She knew his name and he had told her that he was a writer—but she had no proof that he was telling the truth ... men sometimes invented glamorous jobs for ulterior motives. She did not know where he lived ... he might be married ... he might be a dangerous man to know. Yet she was compelled to ask his address so that she could repay him her fare. She must make it very clear that it was her only motive. She did not want him to think that she was unduly interested in him. ...

'Penny for them,' he murmured.

She jumped. 'Oh ...! I was just thinking that

I don't know your address.'

He smiled. 'I'll give you a card.' He produced his wallet and looked through it for a card which he handed to her. She tucked it safely into her bag.

'Thank you. I'll send you the money as soon as I can,' she said, a little embarrassed.

'I understand ... nurses are not paid too well, are they? And the fare to Cumberland ... even single fare ... makes quite a hole in a nurse's salary, I imagine.'

'My father always sends me the money for my ticket home,' she explained. 'But it wouldn't be fair to ask him to pay for my carelessness. I'll be paid at the beginning of the month and I'll send you the money then.'

He nodded. 'I'll look forward to hearing from you.'

'I'm ... I'm not very good at writing letters.' She did not know how else to imply that she thought it would be wrong to enter into any correspondence with him ... and just one chatty letter might be enough to give him the encouragement he might want.

'Neither am I,' he told her lightly. 'It's such a bore, isn't it? I won't expect anything more than a note—does that ease your mind?' He was disappointed that she meant to write finis to an all-too-brief association. No doubt she had her reasons. She might well be engaged or expecting to be ... although she had denied it. Women were not always strictly truthful if the

25

truth might cause a man's interest to wane abruptly ... and she might have wished to encourage him and then changed her mind. Suffering from cold feet in case the boy friend found out, perhaps. . . .

The hospital came in sight as they turned a corner and the taxi began to slow down. Janet turned to him, flushed. 'Thank you so much for everything,' she said shyly. 'You were very kind—and I enjoyed your company on the train.' She held out her hand to him.

He clasped her hand firmly—such a small, neat hand with its delicate bones and smooth skin and almond-shaped nails. 'We had some fun, didn't we?' He smiled at her flushed, pretty face—and he knew that he did not want this girl to walk out of his life so abruptly. Those few hours had been enough to convince him that he could easily come to care for her—if only she would give him the chance. She was quite enchanting and the youthful candour of her lovely eyes caused his heart to behave in the oddest manner. He did not believe in love that came as swiftly and violently as a thunderbolt ... but certainly she was playing havoc with his usually sane and sensible emotions.

'It's a small world,' he added quietly. 'We may meet again.'

'Yes,' she said uncertainly.

He smiled—a warm, attractive smile. 'Shall I contrive to become one of your patients—or will you make it unnecessary for me to go to

26

such lengths?'

Her hand fluttered in his clasp like a small, wild bird. 'I ... I don't know,' she said breathlessly, honestly.

'Perhaps you'll let me know when you write,' he suggested gently. 'That will give you time to make up your mind if you'd like to meet me again, Janet.'

'And give you time to change your mind,' she said impulsively.

He pressed her hand briefly and released it. 'Yes, of course,' he agreed. 'At the moment, it seems a pity that we should part like strangers ... I can't feel that we are strangers, you see. But, as you say, I might change my mind—although it seems very unlikely.' She glanced at the slightly impatient cabby. 'Don't worry about him,' he said lightly. 'Janet, tell me that you want to see me again ... even if you do change your mind by the beginning of next month. We could be friends ... I'd like that.' He smiled with a trace of mischief in his eyes. 'I might need a nurse one day, you know—and it's always a good thing to have useful friends.'

Janet smiled involuntarily. But though her heart was behaving very oddly and his words stirred an impulse to cement a casual acquaintance, she was determined not to be rushed into anything. Janet was a very level-headed young woman ... and, after all, she reminded herself, she was in love with Dominic and should not be feeling this strange

27

attraction for another man.

'I'll write to you,' she said firmly.

'Yes,' he said but he was suddenly withdrawn and cool and she knew that she had hurt him. 'Try not to lose my address,' he added and sat back with a nod to the cabby.

He turned to wave a careless hand as the taxi drove away ... and Janet stood on the pavement beside her case and watched until it was out of sight, her heart strangely heavy and her mind troubled by the fear that she had disappointed him.

She picked up her case and turned towards the Home. She knew that he did not expect to see her again—he would trust her to refund his money but he would be more than surprised if it was accompanied by anything more than a brief note of thanks. Well, it was all very silly to make so much fuss over parting with a complete stranger, she told herself sternly ... heavens, she would have forgotten the man within a few days. And if she really wanted to impress on him that they were merely ships that passed in the night, she could borrow the money from Helen and post it off to him the next day.

He had seemed to like her, had seemed really hurt by her reluctance to meet him again ... but he would probably have forgotten her by the time he reached his destination. No doubt he would be puzzled when the money arrived, the incident completely forgotten, and her name would mean nothing to him. He would have a difficult time trying to put a face to the name. Certainly he was unlikely to wait impatiently for a letter from her ... and she would be the world's biggest fool if she were to imply in any way that she would welcome a further meeting. Two weeks was a very long time ... time enough for anyone to regret an impulsive suggestion ... time enough for anyone to forget a casual encounter on a train....

CHAPTER THREE

Adrian switched off the ignition and turned to smile at his lovely companion. 'Back into harness.'

Helen smiled. She glanced at the tall, familiar building that had virtually been home for the past year and knew a sense of relief. Sanity and security lay behind that raw, modern façade of bricks and mortar.

Adrian produced his cigarette case. Helen shook her head and he busied himself with lighting his own cigarette. 'I won't have much free time for a few weeks,' he said, a little stiffly. 'Saval is on my neck and I must finish the new play.'

'I understand,' she assured him with a faint note of pride. 'You've been very good—it's my fault that you've neglected the play, I know.

We've seen more of each other this last fortnight than for months.'

'You would fall in love with a busy playwright.'

'And I'm a busy nurse,' she countered.

'You chose the life, darling.'

'I don't regret it.'

He sought her fingers for a brief moment. 'I'm glad you have your career, Helen ... I can't give you as much time as I'd like. It's better for you to have your work to occupy your mind—rather than other men and the social round.'

She raised an eyebrow. 'One meets other men even as a nurse ... St. Cecilia's isn't a convent, Adrian.'

He dismissed her words with a faint shrug. 'Sick men—or preoccupied doctors. It isn't quite the same thing. Do you see much of Hammond these days?' he added, almost abruptly.

She looked at him quizzically. 'Jealous?'

'Merely curious.'

'We meet occasionally. But he's virtually engaged to Janet, you know. It's a long time since he gave me a second thought.'

'Do you mind?' He tossed his half-smoked cigarette through the window.

'Why should I? Dominic and I were never anything but friends.'

'He asked you to marry him,' he reminded her.

'Mere habit ... he asked me several times. We both knew it wouldn't work out ... Dominic has a mental image of the perfect wife and for a time he thought I could measure up to it. He certainly wasn't in love with me.'

'You should know.' He leaned forward to brush her cheek with his lips, lips that were cool and fleeting. 'I must rush ... I've an appointment with Saval.' He opened the car door. 'I'll ring you, darling...'

Helen watched the car as it pulled away into the stream of traffic. Her eyes were thoughtful and faintly troubled. She was a tall, slender young woman, strikingly lovely with auburn hair coiled in a neat chignon, her violet eyes fringed by long, dark lashes.

She did not claim to have a vocation for nursing. It was a way of life that offered experience combined with purpose. There was a satisfaction in knowing that she was doing a useful job of work—and doing it well. She enjoyed the life and had made many new friends and found them more loyal, more generous, more worthwhile than the irresponsible, thoughtless crowd of socialites who had once provided her with amusement and entertainment and mild flirtation.

Adrian did not fit into either group. He was different to the men she had known before ... and he still exercised a strong fascination for her. She had met him at one of her mother's famous parties. She had liked the disarming appeal of his smile and the warm admiration of his glance. She had wondered if they would meet again but the weeks had passed and, apart from one brief meeting at a theatre, she had seen and heard nothing of him. Piqued, vaguely disappointed, Helen had tried to dismiss him ... until the day that his car was involved in an accident that would have cost a child's life if he had not acted swiftly and unselfishly. Badly injured, he had been brought into Casualty ... and Helen had been sent to special him until the S.S.O. arrived. In a split second, she had realised that she was in love with a man she scarcely knew.

Later, having received permission to see him, she had stood beside his bed, studying the familiar features. Pale and drawn, the stitches inserted in a nasty gash above his eye were stark against the pallor of his skin. His right leg was in plaster and suspended by a pulley. The rasp of his breathing betrayed the penetration of his lung by a broken rib...

Helen had spoken his name gently and his eyes had flickered briefly. 'Not another injection ...' he had protested. 'I'm not a pin-cushion.' Then he had opened his eyes to recognise her. 'Hallo ... nice of you to call. Sorry I can't give you a drink.'

'Another time.' She had sat down by the bed and allowed him to take her hand.

'Odd that we should meet again ... like this—not as I'd planned. You're very lovely ...

too lovely to forget.'

'Did you try?'

'Yes ... you're young, wholesome, sincere. I've known too many women who lacked your qualities ... I've known too many women— that's why I can't ask you to marry me much as I want to....'

Her heart had lifted with happiness and relief. She had heard of his reputation with women ... but in that moment it did not matter. This was the man she wanted, the man she loved, the man who could give her all she needed—happiness, security, laughter and a richly-endowed love.

'I'll take you as you are,' she had promised, never doubting that he loved as she did—an enriching, fulfilling love that could meet all and any demands.

His recovery had been a slow business. Soon after his discharge, he had given her the diamond solitaire that she wore on her ring finger ... and now, as Helen stood watching his car dwindle in the distance, she twisted that ring absently.

Something was very wrong. In her heart, she knew that Adrian regretted their engagement and that he would never marry her. She believed that he loved her, in his own fashion, but she realised abruptly that the amount of love he could spare for anyone could never be enough to ensure their happiness. It was not Adrian's fault ... he was merely one of those men who were incapable of deep, integral emotion. There had been a succession of affairs in the past ... and Adrian, knowing his limitations, had been quite content that they should never be anything but affairs.

Their love for each other should have been different: it had seemed different in the beginning ... Helen had been sure of his love and its lasting powers, she had been untroubled by his frankness about the women in his past, she had been convinced that she was the one woman he would want for the future. When had things started to go wrong? When had she first noticed the subtle change in his manner, the slow but certain waning of his affection and interest, the frequency of his pleas of work to be done so that they saw less and less of each other?

Helen strongly suspected that he would marry her if she forced his hand—because he still cared enough to be reluctant to hurt her in any way. But how could such a marriage succeed? If his love had lessened so quickly while they were merely engaged it was unlikely that it could regain its original force once they were married. And Adrian might tire of her even more quickly if she was his wife ... he might be restless, impatient, irked by domestic ties. She could never be confident of his loyalty ... and no marriage could survive a constant gnawing anxiety, fierce apprehension, distrust and jealousy.

Adrian was very handsome. He had a compelling and fatal fascination for women and Helen had seen for herself that women threw themselves at his head, flattered and coquetted, tempted and encouraged ... perhaps for the time being he could resist their lures—but for how long?

In his world the marriage vows were often treated lightly and extra-marital affairs were nothing out of the ordinary. Despite her sophistication and the way of life she had always known, Helen was old-fashioned enough to expect that the man she married would always remember his vows ... as she would!

A faint sadness hovered about her lips. No, she did not think that she and Adrian would ever be married—and her sadness was for the crashing of her dreams and not for the soreness of her heart. For Helen knew that her own feelings were not as emotionally and deeply involved as they had been ... she still loved Adrian but now she loved with reservations, she could admit his faults, could view the man coolly and critically and face the future with honesty. Perhaps, after all, the new love was better than the old—which had been flavoured by the romantic illusions of infatuation.

Helen picked up her case and turned towards the hostel. Then, at the sound of her name, she spun on her heel. 'Dominic!' She dropped her case and held out both hands to him, not pausing to analyse the surge of warm pleasure.

His smile was warm for it was a long time since she had seemed so pleased to see him. 'Have you enjoyed your holiday?'

'Very much.' She laughed up at him gaily. 'But I thought we might have run into each other, Dominic—have you been so busy?'

'Our paths probably lie in different directions these days,' he returned smoothly.

'Not entirely! You were invited to dinner the other evening,' she reminded him with faint tartness.

He inclined his head in a gesture of acquiescence. 'Unfortunately I already had another engagement—one of long standing.'

Helen could not have explained why she was so convinced in that moment that he was lying, that he had deliberately turned down her father's invitation, that he had no wish to see more of her than was inevitable. Did he dislike her so much these days? Had she antagonised him so utterly that he felt they no longer had anything in common? She was suddenly conscious that her greeting had been unnecessarily warm—and possibly unwelcome. He had certainly snubbed her in that cool, smooth way of his—and for a moment the old, contemptuous anger flared to life.

'How very convenient!'

'Convenient?'

'You were spared an evening in my company!'

'My dear Helen! Are we out of sympathy at the moment? Have we quarrelled recently? You should have reminded me ... and nothing would have induced me to cross the road to speak to you!' He laughed down at her with easy amusement.

Helen smiled involuntarily. It had been foolish to try to pick a quarrel with him ... she had no grounds for such a quarrel and certainly he was free to keep whatever social engagements he chose. Now she could not even remember why she had been momentarily annoyed with him ... and his laughing, quizzical words scattered her anger to the winds.

She had known Dominic Hammond since she was a mere schoolgirl. At one time she had been madly infatuated with him ... but a meeting with an attractive French boy of seventeen had put an end to her youthful calf-love. Now she liked him well enough but she had always thought it a pity that his looks and undeniable charm should be tempered by arrogance and a cold reserve.

She did not understand why the impulsive, romantic Janet should have fallen so heavily in love with Dominic. Did his arrogance, his air of seeming indifference, evoke a determination to humble him, to awaken warmth and interest in a frigid heart? Had she really succeeded?

Would Dominic really marry Janet? She had been hinting at a possible engagement for the last six or seven weeks—so he must have allowed her to believe that marriage was in his thoughts.

Helen hoped that he had changed his views on marriage during the past year—for she knew Janet well enough to be sure that the type of proposal that Dominic had once offered *her* would not suit the romantic, vulnerable Janet.

Because her friend was in her thoughts, it was perfectly natural to mention her to Dominic. 'Have you any idea what time Janet should be back?'

'Her train reaches Paddington just after five, I believe.' He glanced at his watch. 'Shall we go to the station and meet her? It's such a long journey ... I expect she'll be travel-weary and rather bored.'

Helen hesitated. 'Oh, I don't know that I want to play gooseberry!'

'Don't be silly ... Janet will be thrilled by the reception committee—and I can't be a committee of one!'

She laughed. 'Are you sure you wouldn't rather meet Janet on your own?'

'Quite sure.' He picked up her case, took her by the arm and guided her firmly towards his long, sleek Jaguar that was parked against the opposite kerb.

As they drove through the busy streets towards the station, they exchanged occasional remarks but were for the most part silent. Helen knew that Dominic liked to concentrate on his driving in heavy traffic ... she did not know that his thoughts were of her rather than the road before him.

It had become a habit with Dominic Hammond to think of Helen as his personal property and his future wife long before he asked her to marry him. He had not been deterred by her prompt refusal and her insistence that she did not care for him. One day Helen would realise that they were ideally suited ... one day she would realise the sanity and security of his offer of marriage ... one day she would tire of her flighty way of life and be quite content to settle down happily with him.

Then she had chosen to train at St. Cecilia's—and he had been angry, construing her decision as a cocked snook aimed at himself, resenting the implication that she would rather be a poorly-paid, hard-worked nurse than the wife of a brilliant and successful surgeon. His pride had been hurt rather than his heart for he had never pretended to love Helen. It had seemed very likely to him that they could make a tolerable success of marriage. Affection, understanding, mutual interests and friends, similar backgrounds and a sensible approach to marriage were an excellent foundation—and surely he and Helen possessed these things.

He had not given up his wish to marry Helen

too soon or too easily. He had been convinced that she would soon tire of her whim to be a nurse ... and might very well be ready to listen to another proposal of marriage. Her short spell of training would give them yet another interest in common—and certainly she would be more able to appreciate the demands of his profession.

But things had not worked out that way. Helen loved nursing: she was proving to be a good nurse; she had fallen for that disreputable rake of a playwright and she was planning to marry him. She had never been so unattainable.

And he had allowed himself to become involved with Janet ... sweet, appealing, impulsive, vulnerable Janet who loved him so much that he could do no wrong in her eyes.

It was all very strange.

His emotions had lain dormant since the days of his medical studies when his passionate feeling for a beautiful nurse had been ridiculed and scorned by the girl who paraded her preference for another man. Young and sensitive and deeply hurt, Dominic had vowed that he would never again allow a woman to inflict pain, heartache and humiliation on him.

He had kept that vow ... partly because his work had made so many demands on him that there was little time for women in his life ... partly because he had never met any woman who had disturbed his peace of mind for a moment.

Janet had offered friendship, liking, respect and admiration: there had been a certain appeal in her youth, her *joie de vivre*, her complete lack of coquetry; she had stirred something to life that he had believed to be incapable of resurrection. He had allowed himself to be swept along on the tide of her impulsive and obvious affection for him ... wondering if her warmth and sweetness might prove to erase the bitter memories of Angela.

She had become very dear to him—yet still there was something lacking in his feeling for the young girl. He could not reconcile their affection for each other with a strange conviction that marriage with him was not for Janet. He was not the man for Janet ... and yet it was not a purely unselfish desire to protect her that prevented him from asking her to marry him.

He still could not free himself of the mental image of the wife he wanted ... and Janet was not the woman to measure up to that image ...

Helen glanced at Dominic. His profile was harsh in its arrogance and his mouth held a faint grimness. She wondered at the thoughts that lay behind those dark, inscrutable eyes. He was a difficult man to know, seldom revealing his innermost thoughts or feelings, rarely succumbing to an affectionate impulse, cold, formal and self-sufficient. Was he a different man when he was alone with Janet—

41

and if not, how could she love a man who would surely freeze emotion at its very conception.

She had seen very little of him since her engagement. She had heard of him through Janet, of course—but Janet, being in love, painted an incredible picture of a man that Helen scarcely recognised! Certainly the man that Janet described would have been incapable of a cold-blooded proposal of marriage...

Helen was oddly chilled as she remembered the last occasion when they had gone out together. It was also the last time that he had suggested that she should marry him. There had been a possessiveness in his manner from the moment of their meeting—and within minutes he had contrived to offend by demanding that she should give up nursing (a ridiculous whim and a career to which she was definitely not suited) and marry him. He had assured her that he understood her first refusal ... with a little effort, she could almost recall the exact words:

'If I'd claimed to love you, declared I couldn't live without you, you would have said yes. You're hungry for love—you think it's the be-all and end-all of everything. It isn't. I've tried it once ... once bitten, twice shy, believe me!'

Angrily she had assured him that his proposal, the kind of marriage he suggested, was little more than an insult. Unmoved, he had said that she would marry him yet ... that he could be patient. Helen could not remember a time when she had been more furious with anyone—but she had kept her temper with an effort ... and the remainder of the evening had proved to be quite a success.

Dominic had charm, when he cared to use it. But he was a remote man, living in a cold world of his own, sparing with his affections, rebuffing affection from others, expecting too much, demanding too much ...

It would have been a mistake to marry Dominic—and she had no regrets. But occasionally, very foolishly, she wondered if it might have been possible to stir his sleeping heart, to bring him down from that icy mountain, to make him more human, more lovable. Dominic in love would surely be a different person to the Dominic who was supremely indifferent to all women and was tactless enough to admit it. She might have accepted the challenge if she had not met Adrian and fallen in love with him—and if Dominic had not begun to take an interest in Janet. Now it would never be her doing if Dominic forsook the sanctuary of his private tower of ice ...

CHAPTER FOUR

Arriving at Paddington, Dominic spent a few minutes in finding a parking space. Then they made their way into the terminus with its bustling crowds, shrill voice of the announcer over the tannoy and the flurry of trains arriving and departing.

'We've time for a cup of tea,' he announced when he had checked the arrivals board. 'I hate waiting by barriers.' They crossed the station to the nearest buffet and he pushed open the glass doors for Helen to enter. He followed her in, glanced idly about the crowded room for an empty table and then stiffened involuntarily. He turned to Helen with an urgent hand on her arm. 'It's too crowded—we'll try the other buffet.'

Her glance had followed Dominic's and she swiftly understood his sudden retreat. It seemed that Janet had reached London earlier than expected ... and she was with a very attractive man. They seemed to be on the best of terms, completely abosrbed in each other and their seemingly intimate conversation.

Dominic strode across the station with Helen on his heels. He was neither angry nor jealous that Janet should be enjoying a tête-à-tête with another man—he merely wished to spare her any embarrassment at his unexpected

44

appearance. He was honest enough to admit to himself that he would be relieved to learn that Janet was interested in another man. He would welcome the knowledge. But he thought, rather ruefully, that Janet would probably present him with a perfectly innocent explanation without any prompting on his part. The man might well be an old friend or even a relative—and she had every right to meet him without consulting Dominic or asking his approval or consent.

Helen knew that he was hurt and angry and her ready sympathy went out to him. It was too bad of Janet to play fast and loose with his emotions!

It would not matter if Dominic was merely fond of Janet, if their relationship was based on friendship and liking ... but his abrupt withdrawal and the look in his eyes had convinced Helen that he loved Janet and was dismayed by her intimacy with another man. It was neither just nor merited that he should suffer heartache and humiliation a second time! Any woman would be only too glad to know his love, she thought indignantly—and was oddly surprised by the heat of her indignation.

She reminded herself firmly that she had not wanted Dominic—and the fierce voice of pride protested that he had never been in love with her! His wish to marry her had been marked by decided indifference to her feelings in the matter—and he had made no secret of his lack of love for her. Anyone with an ounce of spirit would have refused such a cold-blooded proposal!

They stood together at the long counter, sipping strong, scalding tea. Dominic produced his cigarette case and offered it to Helen and then gave her a light. 'Janet must have caught an earlier train,' he said easily.

Helen met his eyes, searching for a hint of dismay, the darkness of pain or the steel of anger. But he was in control of his emotions now, she realised—and his dark eyes seemed warm and untroubled. She was silent, uncertain of a suitable reply.

'It doesn't pay to plan surprises,' he went on ruefully. 'One never knows if they will turn out to be as welcome as one hopes.'

'Perhaps Janet wasn't sure of her plans,' Helen suggested diffidently.

'She doesn't have to answer to me for her movements.'

Helen looked at him curiously. She admired and understood his determination to conceal his real thoughts and feelings. 'Do you think that she saw you?'

He shrugged. 'I doubt it. There was no point in intruding—and I don't mean to let her know that I came to meet her, of course. She would be upset that we'd missed each other.'

'I won't mention it, of course,' she assured him swiftly.

He smiled. 'She looks very well. I realise now that she must have been very tired and in need of a holiday—the rest has been good for her.'

'We were all tired,' Helen agreed. 'The exams were a bit of a strain.'

'I'm sure of it ... how did you spend your holiday, Helen? You didn't go away?'

'No ... it was the usual thing—parties, theatres, nightclubs.' She did not realise that her tone was tinged with the remembrance of boredom and weariness. There had been so much of those things in her life and she would have welcomed something different. But her tentative suggestion that they should get away for a holiday had been vetoed by Adrian who apparently never tired of the bright lights and the gay social round.

He nodded and pushed away his empty cup. 'Sorry to rush you but I expect Janet will telephone as promised and I'd like to get back to the house.'

'Yes ... of course,' she agreed hastily and gathered up bag and gloves, leaving the half-empty cup.

'You've time to finish your tea, Helen.' But he glanced at his watch as he spoke.

'I won't bother.' She wrinkled her nose with distaste.

He smiled. 'It wasn't very pleasant, was it?'

They made their way out of the terminus and along the busy pavement to the waiting car. Helen walked by his side in silence. It was

47

obvious that he really cared for Janet. Why else was he so anxious to be home when she telephoned—and so determined that she should not know he had decided to meet her at Paddington and seen her in the company of another man? He must be very anxious to see her and discover from her manner if she intended to end their affair or if she still cared for him. It seemed so out of character for the proud Dominic ... but love could humble the fiercest pride.

She knew that she was unreasonably angry with Janet. The girl was not engaged to Dominic: she had every right to encourage the attentions of other men; that appearance of intimacy possibly had a perfectly innocent explanation—and yet, because Dominic was hurt and puzzled and fearful of losing the woman he loved, Helen was furious with her friend. Didn't Janet appreciate how lucky she was to be loved by a man like Dominic—a man who had not given his heart lightly or easily? Did it really mean so little to her? Despite the impression she had given during the last few months, did she really only care for Dominic as a friend? Helen could have sworn that Janet was in love—but one never really knew the true thoughts and feelings of someone else.

Dominic was particularly vulnerable. It had taken him years to forgive and forget the woman he had once loved and lost. He had become cynical about all emotion. It had needed a girl with Janet's warmth and sweetness to break down that cynicism and melt the icy barrier he had erected about his heart—and it would be too cruel if he had learned to love again only to be hurt again. Janet must not be allowed to hurt him! In some way, she must protect Dominic from hurt and ensure his lasting happiness with the girl he loved!

'You're very quiet,' Dominic commented. 'I hope you don't attach too much importance to a trifling incident?'

She threw him a warmly reassuring smile. 'No, of course not! I haven't given it a second thought.'

He raised a sceptical eyebrow but said nothing.

After a momentary pause, Helen went on: 'I was thinking about St. Cecilia's. I'm looking forward to going back to the wards ... I suppose they've coped without me for the past fortnight but I've missed everything very much.'

'I imagine that a great many of the male staff have managed to concentrate on their work for a change,' he told her drily.

Helen laughed lightly. 'That's rather unkind,' she reproached. 'I never encourage anyone to neglect their work.'

'Encouragement isn't necessary when a young woman is both beautiful and unattainable.'

Colour stole into her lovely face. 'I think you tend to exaggerate, Dominic.' Her tone was slightly indignant. 'It isn't my fault if lack of interest encourages them to think I'm just playing hard to get.'

'I'm teasing you, my dear.' He turned to smile and touched her hand briefly. 'I know that you care for Hart—you've never made any secret of it. You're merely amused by the attentions of other men ... and I think you rather enjoy a little light-hearted flirtation.' He paused and then added, rather stiffly: 'It seems that nursing is your métier, after all, Helen— much to everyone's surprise.'

'Including yours,' she pointed out tartly.

He nodded. 'Including mine. I thought it was a whim, a passing phase. I thought you'd throw in the towel after a few weeks. I admire you for sticking to nursing, anyway—but I suppose St. Cecilia's will lose you very soon now that you're going to be married.'

She turned her head to study the busy pavements. 'Oh, I'm not getting married just yet.'

'Hart must be a very patient man.'

'Yes, he is.' Her tone indicated her reluctance to discuss Adrian Hart and her engagement.

He was silent. He knew that Helen did not give her affections easily—and he wondered why the notorious playwright had succeeded where so many other men had failed. Having

50

met the man, he had not liked him ... he thought him to be weak, unreliable and too generous with his emotions. He seemed to embrace the whole of humanity with a spontaneous affection—and his attitude to Helen was much too casual for a man supposedly in love.

Helen had always been eager for love—and no doubt she had built up Hart's careless affection in her own mind until it reached the desired proportions. Hart was tolerant and easy-going and uncritical—and Helen, always so vulnerable, so quick to suspect criticism, would appreciate these facets of his character. His reputation with women had never been good ... but Helen, like all women, probably believed that he would change because she loved him. Women adored rogues and were easily persuaded that their weaknesses stemmed from bad influences.

Dominic could understand why Helen had fallen so swiftly and impulsively in love with a man like Adrian Hart. But he was conscious of a faint sense of bitterness that she was so willing and eager to marry the playwright when she had spurned *his* sincere and honest wish to marry her. Obviously honesty did not pay in affairs of the heart—and he had often regretted his inability to pretend a love he did not feel. Helen needed to feel that she was loved ... if he had played his cards right she would have been his wife now and in his heart he knew that their marriage would have been happy and successful. But it was much too late for regrets....

He dropped Helen outside the Nurses Home, assured her that they would meet again soon and drove away with a careless wave of his hand.

Helen made her way to the room she shared with Janet and Sally, her active mind turning over ways and means of ensuring his happiness even while common-sense protested that she should not interfere in the affairs of her friends and that she might be worrying unnecessarily.

She had completely forgotten the depression that had settled on her when she parted with Adrian that afternoon. It seemed that she had something more important to think about than her own unsatisfactory engagement now that Dominic's happiness was at stake ... and she did not pause to wonder why she should be so concerned.

She was changing into her uniform when Janet came into their room and threw her case on to one of the beds.

'It's the bad penny!' she announced gaily. 'Did you have a nice holiday? Isn't Sally back yet?'

'Not yet.'

Janet did not notice the curtness of the reply. 'Gosh, I'm exhausted! You look a little pale—too many late nights?'

Helen forced a smile, feeling very much out

of sympathy with her friend. 'I expect so ... we had rather a hectic time.'

'How's Adrian?'

'Very well—and panting to get back to work on the new play. He managed to make me feel thoroughly guilty about dragging him away from it.' Her tone held a note of resentment.

Janet looked at her swiftly. 'Not very kind of him.'

'Oh, it doesn't matter.'

'You didn't change your mind about nursing, then? I was quite prepared to find that you'd decided to get married and not bother with your training any more.'

'My conscience is too active,' she retorted with as much lightness as she could muster. 'I couldn't leave all these poor patients in the lurch—and it's quite obvious that St. Cecilia's would collapse at the foundations if it lost one of its most promising nurses.'

Janet laughed. 'No such considerations brought me back—I lack your staggering conceit, my dear. I loved being at home but it was so quiet and uneventful that I just couldn't stand it any more.'

'Don't tell me you missed the hurly-burly of the wards!' She sat on her bed and studied her long, nylon-clad legs thoughtfully. 'Did you telephone Dominic, by the way?'

Swift colour hurtled to Janet's cheeks. 'Dominic? Yes ... on my way in.'

Helen said easily: 'I met him this afternoon.

He said he was expecting to hear from you as soon as you arrived in London.'

'I'm seeing him tonight.' Her voice was rather strained. She rose and unlocked her case and began to unpack her things, her back to Helen. She was almost dreading the appointment with Dominic ... and that was silly when she loved him. But she could not put Eden Varndell out of her mind too abruptly— and the sight of the crossword book lying just inside her opened case brought him vividly to mind. She stared in dismay at his silver pencil and realised that she had slipped it in her case without thinking. He would surely miss it very soon ... and she must send it back to him. His initials were engraved on the pencil ... E and V intertwined. She opened her bag to check that she had the small card with his address safely in her possession. She took it out ... and it slipped from her unsteady fingers.

Helen stooped to retrieve the small piece of white pasteboard and could not help but see the name and address. 'Eden Varndell!' she exclaimed. 'The writer?'

Janet took the card from her friend with heightened colour. 'Do you know him?'

'I've read his books.' She suddenly realised why Janet's companion at Paddington had seemed so oddly familiar—and she looked at Janet in some surprise.

'I ... I met him on the train,' Janet said stiffly. 'He was ... very nice. I lost my ticket

54

and didn't have enough on me to pay the fare ... so he loaned me the money. That's why he gave me his card ... so I can pay him back.' She stumbled on the words in her endeavour to impart as little importance as possible to them.

'You are a scatter-brain,' Helen merely said indulgently. 'How did you come to lose your ticket?'

'I don't know ... I had it in the mirror pocket of my bag ...' Sudden enlightenment touched her small face. 'Of course! I went to powder my nose on the train ... I remember taking out my mirror so I could see the back of my head after combing my hair. I must have pulled the ticket out with the mirror and didn't notice it fall. Oh, why didn't I think of that! You're quite right, Nell—I *am* a scatter-brain.'

'Never mind ... I expect it will be found and you'll have your money refunded,' Helen comforted.

'Yes ... I hope so, anyway. I can't really afford to lose over two pounds out of next month's salary.'

As she spoke, the third girl who made up the trio of friends came into their room ... and Helen and Janet turned to greet her eagerly.

Sally Calvert was a slight, dark-haired girl, small-boned and rather pretty with her hair curling on her shoulders and the delicate bones of her face hinting at an ethereal charm that would remain long after youthful prettiness had fled.

The only child of elderly parents, brought up rather strictly in their effort to suppress a natural inclination to spoil the long-awaited daughter, she had been extremely shy and ultra-sensitive when she first started her training as a St. Cecilia's nurse but the first year had matured her character and developed her personality in many ways.

'Welcome to the fold,' Helen greeted her, smiling. 'Did you have a nice time?'

Sally nodded. 'Yes, thanks. I was almost sorry to come back much as I enjoy being a nurse. The parents miss me an awful lot, you know.'

'Of course they do! But they must be very pleased that you're doing so well ... they wanted you to train, didn't they?'

'They agreed that it was a good idea and they appreciated how awkward it was for me—and Roger, of course. After all, he lived next door and we couldn't help running into each other almost every day.' She gave a little shrug. 'I was grateful to get away.'

She could talk easily of Roger now but it had been several weeks before she had confided her broken engagement to her new friends.

'He's married now, isn't he?' There was a trace of sympathy in Helen's voice. She often wondered if Sally had really recovered from her love for Roger Gale.

'Oh yes!' she assured Helen and was surprised that she could reply so lightly when her heart had suddenly constricted. Swiftly, defensively, she turned the subject to Helen's own affairs. 'Have you and Adrian fixed the date yet?'

'Oh not yet,' she retorted airily. 'I've told Adrian that I want to finish my training before we get married.'

Sally stared, astonished that anyone so much in love as Helen with her Adrian could view the prospect of a two years wait with equanimity. 'But that won't be for ages!'

'Oh, Adrian doesn't mind waiting. Anyway, I might change my mind ... one never knows. I wonder which wards we'll be on now ... I wouldn't mind going back to Casualty. It's always interesting.' Janet turned from the window. She had been watching a pair of birds on a nearby window-sill and had not taken part in the conversation after greeting Sally.

'Hasn't the list been posted yet?'

'Not yet. We'll find out from Sister Tutor later, I suppose.'

Janet nodded. She could not really muster up any interest—and that was odd for the girl who had always felt so much enthusiasm for nursing.

She began to change into her uniform, her thoughts with Dominic who had been so pleasant, so warmly affectionate on the telephone and whom she had arranged to meet that evening...

CHAPTER FIVE

A fortnight ago, Janet would have been thrilled by the sound of Dominic's voice and her heart would have leaped with a wild joy that vanquished the fear that he might tire of her long before she won his love. But now everything was different...

She wanted to see him, of course—but she shrank from meeting the warmth of affection in his dark eyes and knew that she no longer wanted the strength of his arms about her or the touch of his lips on her own.

While she talked to Dominic, another face had been before her mind's eye and another voice had echoed in her ears—and she was miserably afraid that the memory of Eden Varndell would take a great deal of dislodging. It might never be completely erased from her heart and memory.

It was utterly incredible and the most foolish thing that a level-headed girl like herself could do ... to feel this strong, impetuous need for a man she scarcely knew and might never meet again.

She had to forget him. It should not be difficult ... she had her work and her friends— and Dominic. It scarcely seemed possible that she had forgotten Dominic while she talked and laughed with Eden Varndell and knew the warmth of admiration and interest in his manner. Was she so fickle, so easily swept off her feet by a handsome, personable man?

He was not merely attractive and interesting. There was something else ... something that appealed to her very strongly. A sense of belonging, a feeling of mental and spiritual affinity, an odd certainty that she could place her life in his hands without a qualm.

But she was letting her thoughts run away with her! It was absurd ... he was a comparative stranger and she must not attach too much importance to an impulsive suggestion that they should meet again. It would have been easy, too easy, to agree readily but common-sense had rescued her in the nick of time. Certainly he had exercised a very disturbing influence ... she was still aware that excitement lifted her heart and that every nerve in her body tingled with new life.

She had to remember that his interest could only have been brief and short-lived. It would be foolish to believe that he had been seriously attracted. Her chin lifted with sudden determination. Whatever strange, searing emotions he had brought to life must be summarily dismissed. She reminded herself that she loved Dominic, that she had been thrilled and thankful to realise his growing fondness for her, that it was quite possible that he would ask her to marry him in the near future. He had filled her thoughts and her heart to the exclusion of almost everything else for months now ... he was all she could ever want and if he really wanted to marry her then her cup should be filled to overflowing.

So it was extremely pointless and unnecessary to dwell on thoughts of Eden Varndell for their paths were never likely to cross again—and she did not want him in her life to confuse her emotions and bring doubts that she might not, after all, love Dominic as deeply as she had always believed!

She thrust the thought of Dominic and Eden Varndell away abruptly ... and suddenly conscious that her friends were glancing at her curiously, plunged into sudden gaiety.

'Can you really believe that we've survived the first year? I shall feel an absolute fraud when Sister Tutor gives us our new belts—I *know* I only just scraped through the exams by the skin of my teeth. Still, what a lark to be lording it over the new juniors! We shall be absolute founts of wisdom compared to their sublime ignorance!'

'Ignorance is an enviable state of bliss,' Helen retorted ruefully. 'After all, as second years we shall be expected to know all we've been taught in the first year—and heaven help us if we make silly mistakes as though we were still juniors!'

She was not deceived by Janet's attempt at levity but the troubled look in her friend's eyes incurred her warm sympathy. She was very much puzzled about the whole affair. Janet had claimed to have met Eden Varndell on the journey from Cumberland—but was it really possible for any couple to be on such intimate and affectionate terms in such a short space of time. Helen was an experienced young woman ... it had needed one brief glance only to inform her that the radiance in Janet's eyes and the warmth of her companion's manner hinted at more than casual acquaintance. She did not believe in love at first sight ... that was all very well for romantic fiction writers but such a thing was more likely to be mere physical attraction between two people—an attraction that might become something warmer if it was fed with frequent meetings and the opportunity to know each other better but which was more prone to a swift death in the clear light of sensible thinking.

If Janet had really met the man that afternoon, surely she did not fancy herself in love with him?

Surely she did not mean to break off with Dominic on the strength of one brief meeting with a stranger?

Perhaps she was troubled because a fleeting attraction for another man had warned her that she could not really care for Dominic. Helen devoutly hoped that her friend would not do anything rash. She should give herself time to realise that nothing was likely to come of a chance meeting with a man who moved in different circles to herself—time to forget him and realise that her happiness really lay in loving Dominic and becoming his wife!

'Do you remember that wretched prelim?' Janet demanded, bringing her thoughts back to the present moment with an abrupt jerk. 'Trust me to drop a tray at Matron's feet! I certainly lived up to my reputation for clumsiness that day!'

'Oh, but that was nothing in comparison to your tussle with a locker during Sir Michael's teaching round,' Sally teased. 'That was a masterpiece!'

'So was Kenton's dressing-down,' Janet returned ruefully. 'I wonder if I'll ever live that down. The students still remind me—and ask me when I'm going to enliven their dull day once more. Why do these things happen to me?'

'You were just born with two left feet,' Sally told her, dimpling mischievously.

'Thanks! Anyway, I never filled a dozen hot water bottles with *cold* water!'

Sally turned pink with embarrassment. 'Oh, don't remind me ... my head was really in the clouds that day.'

'Filling them wasn't so bad ... but I've never been able to understand how you could take them round and put them in the beds without noticing that they were cold,' Janet teased.

'The patients soon noticed!'

'You were lucky to have such an easy-going

Sister on Martha Gibbs,' Helen interposed warmly.

'Oh yes! She assured me that I'd soon learn which was the hot tap and which the cold ... and then sailed away with a vague smile.' Sally giggled.

'We had a marvellous time at the Commemoration Ball, didn't we? Didn't they stare when I walked in on Dominic's arm? You could almost hear that long-cherished etiquette shattering into pieces at their feet ...' Janet broke off, embarrassed, forcibly reminded of her former feeling for Dominic and this new, unaccountable attraction for another man.

'Not to mention the lowest of the low being invited to join Sir Henry's party,' Sally said. 'I think that was when everyone realised that you were the mysterious daughter, Nell.'

Helen gave a little shrug. 'Now, of course, it's common knowledge—and most people have forgotten about it. Looking back, it was rather silly to try to keep it a secret. A junior nurse can't really pull any strings because her father is a specialist, after all—but that's what I imagined everyone would think if they knew the truth. Now I know that a nurse is judged by her work and her character—and no amount of string-pulling will make a Sister out of a hopeless nurse.'

They continued with their lively, rather nostalgic recounting of their memories of the early days in the Training School, the first weeks on the wards, the examinations and the memorable patients that they had known until they were recalled to the present by the shrilling of the bell which told them that the evening meal was being served—and then they hustled to add the last-minute touches to face and hair and uniforms before making their way down to the dining-room.

Sally had entered into the spirit of the conversation with gratitude for the respite from her troubled thoughts. She had not expected nor welcomed the unexpected meeting with Roger that day—and the brief encounter had only served to reawaken thoughts and feelings that were better dead.

Roger Gale had always been an important part of her life. The son of their immediate neighbours, she could not remember a time when she had not known and loved him. He was a tall, good-looking young man with a great deal of charm and a passion for cars. Their engagement had been almost inevitable and had pleased both families who had applauded their decision to wait until they had saved enough money to ensure a good beginning to their married life. Sally had been content to wait, secure in Roger's love, full of dreams for the future ... and then Roger had explained that he was in love with her closest friend and could not marry Sally. She had not even known that he and Mavis liked each other—and she was hurt by the realisation that they had been meeting for some months in secret.

Sally realised that if he had cared more he would have been impatient for marriage: she was honest enough to admit that he had merely drifted into an engagement because they had known each other so long and so well—but she had loved him and it had never occurred to her to doubt his love for her.

Since she went to St. Cecilia's, she had seen Roger only briefly and in passing and they had not exchanged more than mere, embarrassed courtesies. At first the occasional encounters had been painful for Sally: later they had merely brought a pang of nostalgia; later still, she had felt nothing but mild interest in the man she had once loved. It had been inevitable that they would meet and she was proud of her composure and easy manner when they did.

She had been so certain that he no longer meant anything that the sudden turmoil of emotion within her was almost frightening. If only she had not seen him that afternoon. . . .

Walking through a slight drizzle of rain to the station, he had overtaken her in his small, scarlet sports car and stopped to offer her a lift. There had been no reason to refuse and his friendly smile had been disarming.

Sitting beside him in the familiar, once-loved car, she stole a glance at his handsome profile, the strong hands on the wheel and the old tweed jacket which he could not bring himself to discard—and she was overwhelmed by a sudden urge of tenderness and affection.

'Miserable weather.' Sally had abruptly sensed that he was ill at ease. It was so unlike Roger to mouth trivial conventionalities. 'Looking forward to going back?'

'Yes, very much.'

'How are you getting on? I can't imagine you as an efficient nurse.'

'I don't suppose I'm particularly efficient but I do like nursing.'

'I thought you'd be running the place single-handed by now,' he teased—and for a brief moment the light-hearted intimacy of the past had touched them both.

'How's Mavis?' She had not intended to put that abrupt question. The words had slipped off her tongue—and left her stiff with embarrassment.

'Oh, she's fine. Expecting a baby—did you know?'

'Yes, I heard. Your mother told my mother.'

She had known a fierce spurt of jealousy. Roger and Mavis had been married for almost a year and her father had provided the deposit for a house for the newly-weds. Sally had been very bitter about that swift wedding for he had always been so content to wait indefinitely for their proposed marriage. It seemed wrong that Mavis should have gained so much through deceit and the cold-blooded indifference to

Sally's feelings ... Roger, a lovely house and now a baby soon to be born.

'I suppose you knew that Mr. Winton put up the deposit for our house? He's been pretty good to me.' It was almost as though he had read her thoughts.

'Yes ... I'm glad.' What else was there to say?

'Now he's offered to lend me the capital to open my own garage. I thought he might have done it months ago but I suppose he was waiting to see what kind of husband I'd make Mavis. I've got my eye on that place on the Brighton Road—remember? It's a bit decrepit but I can do a lot to modernise it, bring in the motorists. Jennings is all right but old-fashioned and I'll be stuck there for years if I don't branch out on my own now. In three years I'll be able to pay Winton back and open up another garage ... I've worked it all out!'

'That's marvellous!' She had tried desperately to sound sincere. She was pleased for him—despite everything, he was the Roger she had known and loved for years and she could not resent his good fortune. She only hoped that things were not being made too easy for him—that he would not become spoiled and grasping, over-ambitious and too ready to turn to Mr. Winton for financial assistance. 'Everything seems to be working out for you.'

'My guardian angel has suddenly

remembered my existence.' His tone had been almost complacent. 'How about you, Sally—I gave you a rotten deal and I hope things are going better for you now.' It seemed that the words were forced reluctantly from him.

She had tilted her chin proudly. 'You don't have to worry about me!'

'No ... but I do sometimes. I despised myself for hurting you like that—and I'd give anything to believe that you've got over me and found someone else.'

'Need we talk about it?'

He had said quietly: 'There isn't any point in talking about it ... in regretting—anything, is there? But I want you to know that I'm sorry, darling.'

'Save your endearments for Mavis!' She had been furious with him—and with herself for the melting warmth in her heart and the sudden leap of hope that he might have realised his mistake in breaking off their engagement. She knew that his endearment had slipped out unconsciously, due to long habit, but it had stabbed her with painful memory of the days when she had loved to hear it on his lips.

He had muttered something that might or might not have been an apology and then they had turned into the station forecourt.

Glancing at his set, almost unhappy profile, Sally's annoyance, always transitory, had evaporated swiftly. 'I'm sorry, too, Roger. But it turned out for the best, you know. I really love nursing and I'd have missed a great deal if we'd been married as we planned.' As he turned to her with his brilliant, boyish smile the old, dormant love had flared into life again. 'You are happy, Roger?' she had asked wistfully.

'Oh, sure! I've got everything I wanted,' he had retorted flippantly and she had been shocked by the biting bitterness of his tone. He had glanced at his watch. 'You don't want to miss your train, Sally.'

'No ...' She was vaguely dissatisfied with this abrupt parting. 'Thank you for the lift.'

He had shrugged. 'I was driving this way.'

'Well ... perhaps I'll see you next time I'm home.'

'Perhaps I'll see you in London,' he had returned evenly. 'I'm coming up to talk business with the chap who owns the garage ... I'll give you a ring. We could have lunch together.' Typical of him that he suggested and did not request ... that he did not wait for an answer but accepted her agreement as a matter of course.

Sally had been startled—and then she had been aware of fierce heat in her cheeks. For there had been a hunger in his eyes that touched her heart despite all her resolutions and then she knew that he did regret all that had happened in the past year.

She had said recklessly: 'I'd like that, Roger.'

His hand had clasped hers for the briefest of

moments. Then Sally had scrambled from the car, took her case from his hand and hurried into the station, too nervous, too excited, to find words to bid him goodbye.

She had not dared to think of him during the short journey to Victoria. Later, she had been grateful for the company of her friends which prevented the thoughts from crowding with determination into the forefront of her mind.

Yet now, sitting over the meal with the hubbub of voices about her and the clatter of cutlery and china echoing in her ears, the thoughts were too strong for her will-power and she relived again that encounter with Roger.

She knew that she had never ceased to love him. She had merely learned to discipline her thoughts and emotions, to stifle the memory of him with work and yet more work.

Her quickened heartbeats, the fierce heat in her blood, the sinking feeling in her stomach and the incoherency of her thoughts were all symptoms of a reawakened emotion. She must not love him still ... he was a married man, his wife was expecting his child, everything had been finished between them long ago.

Would he really get in touch with her when he came to London? Did she really want to hear from him, to meet him by arrangement, to co-operate with him in deceiving Mavis—for she knew in her heart that he would not dream of telling Mavis of their meeting.

Against all reason, all common-sense, all instinctive warning of danger, Sally knew that she did want to see him, would see him if the opportunity arose, would deceive Mavis even though deceit had always been alien to her character.

She argued that Roger was not happy in his marriage—that everything had gone wrong for him although he might be in a position to realise some of his ambitions. At last he was beginning to discover that the achievement of a dream was a hollow success if he did not have the girl who had shared the dream to share the reality.

Poor Roger ... had he only married Mavis because she had a wealthy father who could help him realise his ambitions? Sally was very much afraid that she had stumbled on the truth—and she was too much in love and too blinded by that love to criticise the man who had taken such a foolish step. If only there was some way to help him find the happiness he craved ... Sally did not pause to consider the girl he had married for such selfish reasons or the baby she was soon to have. She could only hug to herself the knowledge that Roger had never ceased to love her, after all—that had been evident in all he had said, every glance, every smile ... and his promise to get in touch with her at his first opportunity in a bustling city where it was unlikely that they would meet anyone they knew ...

CHAPTER SIX

Janet listened to the pealing of the bell within the house. Her heart was thumping uncomfortably. She had not seen Dominic for over a fortnight ... the longest space of time since they had become such close friends.

She wondered if the sight of him would steady her wavering emotions and vanquish the thought of Eden Varndell completely—or if it would merely serve to confirm the tiny prick of doubt in her heart.

Travers opened the door and greeted her with his usual punctilious courtesy. Janet was conscious of the familiar suspicion that he neither liked nor approved of her. Probably he thought that she was too young and immature for a man like Dominic Hammond!

Dominic was standing on the threshold of the sitting-room. She smiled at him a little uncertainly. For a long moment he looked at her as though he had never seen her before and Janet could not know that he was cursing himself for a fool! She was a sweet child ... but no more. How had it happened that he had become emotionally involved with a girl with whom he had virtually nothing in common?

He looked into those shining, honest eyes— and all the hopes he had known since he had seen her at Paddington with an unknown man died abruptly. If she wanted to end their friendship, if she had learned to care for another man, she would not be so tremulously and obviously glad to see him again. He could not hurt this vulnerable child. She was in love with him, as he had feared—and he could not reject the generous, loyal, wholehearted offer of her love without a thought for her distress and humiliation. Janet was very sweet and he was exceptionally fond of her ... perhaps they could build a successful marriage on these foundations and perhaps it would put an end to his foolish need for the unattainable.

It seemed an eternity to Janet before he moved towards her and caught her hands, smiling down at her with affectionate warmth. In that long, intent gaze, she had seen the love and the tenderness that he felt for her: his eyes had told her how much he had missed her, how much he needed her—and she could only marvel that she had evoked so great an emotion in a man whose reputation had been one of cool indifference to women. Despite all those silly thoughts in her head, the rebellious murmurings of her foolish heart, she must never say or do anything to cause Dominic to suspect that her love had lessened. She must dismiss Eden Varndell completely from her mind and heart ... and determine to love Dominic as deeply and as single-mindedly as once she had believed she did.

The touch of his hands was reassuring. So

was the deep affection of his smile and the warmth of his voice as he welcomed her quietly: 'It's good to see you, Janet, my dear. I was afraid that your love for Cumberland might keep you there.'

She managed to laugh, a husky, tremulous note that caught at his heart. 'Cumberland will still exist when I've finished my training.'

He drew her into the sitting-room, turned to tell Travers to bring coffee and then sat down by her side on a long, comfortable couch. 'You look very pretty with those Cumberland roses in your cheeks,' he told her lightly. 'A bonny country lass ... it's a pity that they'll fade so soon in this grimy London air.'

'Have you been busy?'

He gave a slight shrug. 'Busy enough. Our profession is very demanding, after all. But I like to be busy.'

Janet sensed the loneliness behind the quiet words. Her ready sympathy was stirred and her determination was strengthened. Whatever her own feelings, it was obvious that destiny had planned that she should assauge Dominic's loneliness, bring new purpose into his life, gladden his days with the joy of loving and being loved.

He was still the man she had always admired and respected so much, the man whose integrity and brilliance and skill filled her with faint awe, the man whose personal magnetism and mature good looks had impressed her so much in those early days. He was all that any woman could want in a man ... and she must count herself fortunate that he had chosen to love her rather than anyone else. If he wanted to marry her—and with a sinking heart she thought that it must be so—then she would try to make him a good and loyal wife.

There was no future in weaving fanciful daydreams about a man she would never see again—in any case, it was so foolish when she did not even know if the man was seriously attracted—and why should he be when they were worlds apart.

She reminded herself fiercely of the days when Dominic had inhabited all her world, when she had been in heaven because he had evinced his liking, had taken her out and flouted hospital etiquette because her attraction was stronger than his fear of disapproval. Those days could not mean so little to her now. Dominic loved her—and so she must convince him that she loved him with all her heart. She simply could not hurt this kindly, generous man.

Surely it was enough to love him a little, to feel a tender pity for the loneliness he had always known, to admire and respect him so greatly, to feel proud and yet humble because he had chosen to love her.

Coffee was brought by the inscrutable Travers and Janet attended to the cups with hands that were a little unsteady.

Dominic reached for a cigarette from the box on the table. She was nervous. Did she feel guilty because she had found someone else and did not want to hurt him? No, that could not be an avenue of escape! He realised only too well that there was no other man in her life. She had given her heart to him and he would never forgive himself if she was to be hurt by him in any way. Perhaps his own lack of love showed through although he was determined to maintain his former easy manner that was tinged with affection and a certain tenderness. It should not be so difficult. He did feel affection and tenderness for Janet. *She* had not changed. She was still the warm-hearted, sweet-natured, generous and candid girl who had kindled to new life an emotion that had been long-dead. He had believed that he was incapable of caring for any woman since Angela had disappointed him so greatly. Janet had proved that it was otherwise ... and it was rather ironic that his affection for her should break down the barrier and allow a stronger, greater and miserably futile love to invade his heart.

Janet need never know that she was second-best. After all, she might yet prove to be the best for him, anyway. One's life was mapped out by a wiser, more perceptive, farther-seeing hand than man's ... and it was no doubt his destiny to marry this vulnerable, youthful girl and give up the absurd and hopeless dreams of another woman.

He encouraged Janet to talk of her holiday, her home, her parents and her brothers. He listened with an interest that was not assumed and his kindly promptings, his swift amusement, his murmurs of approval and understanding all helped to put Janet at her ease. It was not very long before she was chatting away to him without any embarrassment or awkwardness ... and again she thought how kind, how understanding, how sympathetic he was. She could not do wrong if she were to marry him. He would be a good husband. He would love her and cherish her and care for her and do all in his power to ensure her happiness. He had the advantage of maturity and would not make the mistakes in marriage that a younger, less experienced man might make.

She told him of her mother's firm conviction that she did not get enough to eat, of the piled plates and the injunctions to build herself up before going back to hospital food, of the insistence that Janet had lost a great deal of weight, of the anxious enquiries about the comfort of her bed, the amount of sleep she had, the demands she had to fulfil on the wards. She painted an endearing picture of a mother who could not accept that her only daughter was old enough to venture out alone into the world and feared any amount of evils that might befall her.

She told him of her father, the kindly, over-worked doctor who really cared about his patients, bore patiently with his wife's anxious concern for his health and his well-being and continued to do all the things that she insisted he should not do at his age. Dominic had heard a great deal about Janet's father and liked all he had heard. He hoped that it would not be long before he met her family—and the thought reminded him that he might meet them as Janet's husband. Firmly, he suppressed an instinctive recoil from the thought.

She told him of her two brothers: Gil with his rapid succession of girl-friends and racy, light-hearted flow of chatter; Danny, the youngest and still at school, who had already made up his mind to be an architect but at present lived only for cycling and swimming.

Dominic listened and knew that he and this girl were worlds apart ... in background, interests, knowledge of the world, maturity and hopes for the future. Janet loved nursing but she would surrender her career gladly to be his wife and, possibly, the mother of his children. He looked into the years ahead and saw Janet, plump, motherly, domesticated, absorbed in home and family, fussing over him and any children they might have—and it was almost ludicrous that he was seriously considering such a prospect. For any other man she would be a wonderful wife. For himself—Dominic Hammond, brilliant, sophisticated, ambitious, loving a woman who was the absolute epitome of the ideal he had created in his heart ... it was out of the question!

What could he give Janet? Neither love nor passion. Affection, liking, understanding, tolerance, tenderness—were these things enough? Janet was not lacking in perception—could she possibly be happy in such a marriage?

His thoughts gnawed at the problem like a dog with a bone. It would not be consistent with his cherished integrity to marry Janet on such terms. On the other hand, he could not bring himself to hurt the sweet, appealing and very vulnerable girl by bringing their affair to an end.

Janet did not notice his preoccupation with his thoughts. It was a relief to talk of her home and family, of St. Cecilia's and mutual friends—it was safe ground and conversation on such lines certainly prevented him from introducing the subject of their personal affairs. If only it was possible to keep their friendship on such a light and easy basis indefinitely ... at least until she had resolved her rebellious heart.

Without thinking, she mentioned the long and tiring journey from Cumberland ... and at the reminder of her travelling companion, fierce colour flooded her cheeks.

Dominic did not notice. He was wondering whether to mention his intention of meeting her at Paddington. Her reference to the journey gave him a lead.

'You caught an earlier train than you'd intended,' he said evenly.

She nodded. 'There didn't seem to be any point in delaying my return. I had to come back ... my mother was rather upset about it ... so I decided not to prolong her agony.' She looked at him quickly, struck by a sudden thought. 'You didn't go to meet me, Dominic?'

A lie could serve no purpose. 'Well, yes, I did. Helen went with me. You said in your letter that your train reached Paddington just after five—and I knew you wouldn't feel like another journey on public transport.'

'I am sorry,' she said contritely. 'It just didn't occur to me that you might meet the train.'

He shrugged. 'No matter ... it was pretty obvious that you'd travelled earlier than you originally intended. Helen and I had tea in the buffet and then drove back to the hospital.'

She stiffened slightly. 'In the buffet? I didn't see you.'

'I expect you were on your way back to the hospital at the time.'

'Oh ... yes. But I went to the buffet for some tea—and the train was late. So we must have just missed each other.'

Dominic wondered if he only imagined that note of relief in her voice. 'Quite probably,' he

80

agreed easily. He was vaguely disappointed. Having given her such an excellent lead, he had fully expected her to mention that she had met a friend, either by accident or arrangement. The fact that she seemed embarrassed and reluctant to talk about the matter indicated that she did not want him to know of that meeting. It was none of his business, of course—but Janet was usually so open that it seemed a little out of character. She could not know that she had been seen but knowing that he had been at the station it must occur to her that it was possible that her rendezvous with another man had been witnessed. 'It isn't important,' he assured her.

'I'm sorry that you had the journey for nothing.'

He smiled, touched by her obvious contrition and dismay. 'I had an hour to spare—and it seemed an excellent use for it. I wanted to surprise you but I'm quite old enough to know that surprises rarely succeed and are not always welcome.' He changed the subject. 'Back on the wards tomorrow?'

'Yes ... I'm to report to Out-Patients,' she said eagerly.

'Not very exciting,' he commented.

'Oh, I don't mind. I always feel rather sorry for those poor people ... sitting on those benches and waiting hours to see a doctor. Surely someone could work out a new system, Dominic? There isn't much point in giving a patient an appointment at ten o'clock in the morning if he's still waiting for attention at three o'clock in the afternoon.' Her tone was indignant.

'It's unfortunate, I agree—but unavoidable. Your patient is probably waiting to see a specialist who has been tied up on the wards all day—or a surgeon who has been in the theatre since early morning dealing with emergencies. Whenever it's practicable, he will be seen by one of the housemen—but even then it might be decided that the specialist or the surgeon ought to see him when he's free.'

'Yes, I know.' She gave a tiny chuckle. 'I've always wondered if that's why they're called patients, Dominic—because one certainly needs to be patient in that Department.'

He touched her cheek briefly with his fingers. 'You may have a point there.' He glanced at the clock. 'I don't want you to go but it's getting late and I doubt if you have a late pass.'

'Heavens, it is late!' she exclaimed, leaping to her feet. 'Home Sister will scalp me!'

'No, she won't,' he assured her. 'It won't take ten minutes to drive you to the Home. You'll make it by the skin of your teeth.'

As they drove through the quiet streets, Janet was abruptly ill at ease again. She could enjoy herself while they talked of trivial things ... but the moment she was conscious of a certain intimacy in the atmosphere she was uncomfortable. She dreaded the moment of parting when he was sure to kiss her ... it seemed incredible now that she had once lived for his kisses and snatched at the occasional caress as proof that he did indeed love her.

He pulled into the kerb outside the Home and half-turned in his seat to look at her. She was silent and pale—and he told himself that he had been inconsiderate to insist on a meeting that night after her long journey to London. He scarcely knew why he had insisted. Because he had hoped to find a change in her, some evidence that she no longer cared for him? Because he wanted to give her the opportunity to admit that there was someone else if it was true? Or because he had known that the first sight of her would confirm his own belief that love did not come into his feeling for her—and that she could never mean as much to him as the woman he loved and needed so desperately....

With a gentle hand, he brushed a dark curl from her brow and she gave him a wan smile. 'You're tired, darling,' he said tenderly.

'A little,' she admitted.

'You should have had an early night. It wasn't very considerate of me to insist on seeing you this evening.'

'Oh, but I wanted to see you.' She blurted the words impulsively—and was thankful for the shadows that concealed the swift rush of colour to her cheeks. It had been vital that she should see him as soon as possible ... the evening spent with him had clarified her emotions as she had hoped but the result had dismayed her. She knew now in all honesty that she had been in love with love rather than with Dominic Hammond ... now it was a dead feeling that weighed heavily on her spirits.

'Sweet ...' He leaned forward to brush her lips fleetingly with his own.

There was something cool and remote in that brief kiss and Janet snatched eagerly at a vague thought that leaped to her mind. Was it possible that she had been wrong ... that Dominic did not really love her? Did any man treat the woman he loved with a certain indulgent tenderness as though she were a beloved child?

'Dominic ... I wish I knew if you really loved me—or not,' she faltered.

He was silent for a long moment. Now was the time to be honest—to admit that she was very dear to him but not the woman he loved—to banish those dreams from her eyes and the radiance from her smile and the happiness from her heart as once Angela had banished his dreams, his radiance, his happiness. He could not do it ... he could not condemn this sweet child to the heartache and misery that he had known.

He gathered her into his arms and held her very close, understanding the apprehension that had prompted her hesitant question.

'I love you, Janet—very much.' It was not a

lie. He did love her ... as one loved a dear friend—and he had to make that enough to ensure her happiness.

Her heart stopped for a moment and then sank miserably. She had known but still hoped against hope ... it was entirely her fault—she had believed herself in love with him, she had betrayed her feelings time and again, she had prayed that he might come to love her in time ... and now he did and she could only suffer that loving embrace and face up to the knowledge that he wanted her to be his wife.

Dominic hated his immunity to her youthful appeal—and he kissed her with fierce, simulated passion to protect her from the knowledge of his indifference. This was not the woman he yearned to hold in his arms—but that woman was not his and never would be now.

He did not notice that Janet was oddly unresponsive—and she could only hope that he would believe her lack of response was due to natural weariness. What on earth was wrong with her! This was Dominic ... the man she had once loved and hoped to marry with all her heart! Once his kisses had opened the door to a new and wonderful world—only a schoolgirl would feel that the longed-for paradise was no longer what she wanted! Perhaps it was true that she was tired ... too tired to think straight, to sort out the bewildering confusion of emotions. Everything would be different in the morning—no, not different . . . as it used to be!

Dominic was utterly miserable. She was young and lovely and any other man would find her extremely desirable and consider himself fortunate. She loved him . . . and the knowledge of that love, so unselfish, so undemanding, so patient, humbled him. He did not deserve her love, had done nothing to merit it, could never live up to it—but he could ensure that he never earned her contempt or brought unhappiness to her unsuspecting, innocent heart . . .

CHAPTER SEVEN

Eden was puzzled by the intensity of this new, strange emotion that still tormented him. He could not rid himself of a sense of loss, of a fierce, insistent longing to see the girl again.

There had been many women in his life . . . many more sophisticated, more beautiful, more worldly—but not one of them possessed the refreshing innocence, the appealing candour, the ability to stir strange, sweet emotion to life so swiftly, that he had found in Janet Finlay.

One smile, one warm glance from her lovely eyes, had captivated him and he could not forget her. She had released some spring within him that threatened to become a flood that

86

might carry him to a deeper, greater, more moving experience than he had ever known.

It was useless to tell himself that she did not share his feelings or she would have been in touch with him in some way. He had hoped that her discovery of his silver pencil in her case would bring a letter or a telephone call and the promise of its return. He did not even know that she would refund the money he had so swiftly provided for her fare—not everyone was as honest as he hoped and he knew really nothing about the girl.

It was useless to remind himself that he was a grown man and not a callow, inexperienced youth. He continued to cling to the hope that a satisfactory ending could come about from a trite, unimaginative beginning ... a casual encounter with a pretty girl on a train.

This wild, impossible love for a stranger baffled him completely. All because she had smiled, been friendly, encouraged his interest—and then unexpectedly become shy and apprehensive as though she regretted her friendliness and feared to set in motion something she could not command as she wished. His very intensity, his obvious wish to follow up the chance meeting, had frightened her—and it was too late to wish that he had been more restrained, more casual.

With all his experience, he should have known that he was rushing his fences ... these affairs needed to progress at their own leisurely pace—affairs that only promised friendship and affection in time. A foolish, impetuous infatuation, a passing physical attraction, a swift-leaping fascination that cooled with equal swiftness might all demand urgency and recklessness. But his feeling for Janet Finlay had nothing in common with any of these past experiences.

Thirty-two years old, attractive and personable, a bachelor with ample income to maintain his lovely old house, reliable servants and the kind of life that he enjoyed, Eden Varndell, writer and man about town, could not believe that he had fallen headlong in love with an unknown girl.

It was incredible, impossible, something that just could not happen outside the realms of romantic fiction! He was a man of the world, adult, intelligent, experienced—what possible appeal could a young girl have for him? A mischievous, youthful nurse who chattered about her work, her friends, her family to a man she had never seen before. Her youth, her prettiness, her warm personality had enchanted him briefly ... when he left her he had told himself that within a few hours her image would fade and he would probably have the devil's own job to remember her name....

Yet it had not happened. It was almost a fortnight since that meeting on a train and he had not forgotten her. She filled his dreams, his every waking thought. He was sleeping badly, had no appetite for the excellent food cooked and served by his staff, could not muster interest in his writing, his friends, his social life. His nerves twanged in concord with the telephone bell. He searched hastily through his mail for the letter that never came. He was always on edge, short-tempered and impatient, an impossible companion for anyone ... including himself. If this was love—this misery, this sickness of the soul, this incessant ache of longing—then he understood and sympathised with the great lovers of history for the first time in his life. There was no pleasure, no content, no joy in loving a girl who had forgotten his very existence—and who had no reason to remember it.

He sat at his desk in the large, pleasant study, the bright sunshine streaming through the open window. His typewriter was before him and a blank sheet of paper was inserted ready for his pleasure. It had been awaiting his attention for the past hour but he had lost all interest in his work for the time being.

The door opened and he was startled by the unexpected movement, so deep in thought had he been.

His sister raised a quizzical eyebrow. 'You almost jumped out of your skin, Eden ... what on earth is wrong with you these days?'

'Nothing.' He took a cigarette from the box on his desk and thrust it between his lips.

Davina Varndell sat on the edge of his desk

and swung her long, elegant, nylon-clad legs. 'You're not well, Eden ... in fact, you look positively ill lately. Why not see a doctor?'

He gave a short laugh. 'Find one who can cure my complaint and I will!'

The colour receded abruptly from her attractive face. 'Eden! Not you, too—oh God no!'

He stared at her in bewilderment. Then he realised her fear ... their mother had died of cancer some ten years before and now he appreciated the stupidity of his words.

He rose swiftly and touched her shoulder with a reassuring hand. 'Sorry, darling—it was a silly remark to make. I didn't mean to frighten you. No, nothing like that—thank God.'

'Then what did you mean?' she pressed.

He smiled ruefully. 'Ever been in love, Davina?'

She stared. 'No—I don't think so.'

'Then you haven't any idea of the hell that I'm going through.'

It was so unexpected that she began to laugh—and her laughter filled the room until she saw the grimness of his eyes and the tightness of his mouth. She broke off abruptly. 'Darling, how callous of me! It obviously isn't funny if it can play such havoc with your nerves. It was just ... the relief.'

He stubbed the half-smoked cigarette with a fierce, impotent gesture. 'No, it isn't funny.'

She held out her hand to him. 'Eden—do you care to tell me about it?'

He turned away from her, walked to the window and thrust his hands into his pockets. 'There isn't much to tell. It would be ludicrous if it wasn't so damned painful.'

'Who is she ... anyone I know?'

'No ... I hardly know her myself,' he returned curtly.

She looked at his broad, oddly despondent back and her eyes softened. 'There is a cure, you know—or so the cynics have it. Marriage.'

'Out of the question.'

'But why? Darling, you're a very eligible bachelor—I know a dozen women who'd give their eye teeth to marry you!' A sudden thought struck her. 'She isn't ... married, darling?'

'I shouldn't think so—she's a nurse.'

'A nurse! But where on earth did you meet a nurse?'

'On a train.'

'On a train ...?' she repeated incredulously. He swung to face her angrily. 'Is it so fantastic?'

'No ... of course not,' she assured him hastily. 'But—my dear, you never use trains ... you loathe them!'

'I had to leave my car in Cumberland, you may remember. Some trouble with the carburettor—and I had to get back for a literary dinner.'

'And you met this . . . nurse on the train?'

'That's right.'

'Well, darling—forgive me if I'm obtuse—but where's the difficulty? Has she refused to marry you? Perhaps it's a little soon . . . it's only about a fortnight since you came back from the Saxbys, after all.'

'I haven't seen her again.'

'Oh . . . !' She was silent.

The room was filled with their silence until it became intolerable. Eden broke it by crossing to his typewriter and wrenching the empty sheet of typing paper from the machine.

'I can't work . . . impossible to concentrate. I can't sleep. I can't bear to talk to people—I'm unfit for social intercourse. It's incredible, isn't it? A girl I've met once and will probably never meet again! I might be sixteen instead of thirty-two! Davina, I'm in love for the first time—and it's killing me!'

'Why don't you do something about it?' she suggested sensibly.

'What do you suggest?' His tone was ironic.

'Do you know her name?'

'Yes . . . it's Janet—Janet Finlay. Her home is in Anstey Moor.'

'Is she nursing in London?'

'At St. Cecilia's.'

'Then, my dear Eden, if you know so much about her why on earth don't you get in touch with her? This is really amazingly stupid of you, darling. Why, you may not even like the

92

girl once you see her again—you've simply talked yourself into being in love with her because you were attracted and you haven't taken the opportunity to find out if she's really as nice as you thought.'

'What opportunity?' he asked bitterly. 'I asked if I could meet her again and she promised to think about it and let me know. There hasn't been a word from her.'

'Oh dear! It does sound as though she isn't interested, darling,' she said ruefully.

'Exactly!' He paced the room. 'I shall get over it. Just leave me alone, Davina—and bear with me for the time being.'

'I think you would be very wise to have a hectic affair with someone else,' she told him shrewdly.

'Thanks very much!'

She shrugged. 'You never would take advice from anyone.'

'I like to resolve things in my own way.'

'Yes, I know.' She stood up and went towards the door. 'Well, I'm thankful that it's nothing worse, Eden. I've been worried to death in case you were ill.'

'Davina!' She turned in the act of closing the door. 'I'm sorry I've been so difficult. It's helped to talk about it, anyway—thanks.'

She smiled with warm affection in her eyes. 'If I was suffering as much as you are I'd do something about it, darling. I didn't think you were such a defeatist.' And she left him to ponder her words...

Try as he might, Eden did not see what he could do. He could not thrust his attentions on a girl who had proved her lack of interest. He could not forget her or cease to love her—for he had tried. He could not bring himself to take Davina's advice although there were women in plenty who would be willing to embark on an affair with him—he knew in his heart that he would be left with a feeling of disgust that he had sullied the memory of a girl whose innocence and integrity shone in her eyes.

He could only continue to hope that the end of the month would bring a letter from Janet Finlay. He was not concerned with the money she owed him except as a reason for her to write to him. When that letter came ... if it came ... he would reply with all speed. And her letter would give him a lead to his future steps ... if it was stilted and formal he would know that it wrote finis to his hopes and dreams. If it was warm and friendly, more than just a brief note of thanks, he would accept it as the encouragement he needed so much.

In the meantime, he had to stifle his agony of longing in some way—and he returned to his desk, inserted a fresh virgin sheet of paper and forced himself to work on the new novel. It was rubbish and he knew it—but it was a way of passing the lonely, empty, aching hours....

Janet hesitated by the big gates. The house was large and imposing enough to fill her with a sudden panic. What had possessed her to travel into the heart of Buckinghamshire on her free day merely to return a silver pencil and a handful of money? It would have been wiser and safer to return them by post with a brief, formal note of thanks.

She had determined to forget Eden Varndell—yet at her first opportunity she had deliberately set out to see him again. It was a very silly thing to do. He would not know who she was or why she had called on him! A reminder would prove embarrassing to them both.

Sick with excitement and apprehension, the train journey had seemed endless, the walk from the station along leafy, peaceful roads had been a penance—and now she was actually at the gates of the house that stood in its own lovely grounds, she was rooted by the knowledge of her folly and impertinence. She had no right to intrude into his house or his affairs. She had no real reason or explanation for making the long train journey to Raisney St. Mary to arrive unannounced, unexpected and possibly unwelcome.

As she stood, hesitant and very pale, trying to pluck up the courage to walk towards the house, to ring the bell, to hand the pencil and the envelope containing the money to the servant who opened the door, somebody came out of the house and began to walk briskly down the drive towards Janet. It was a woman

... tall, slender and very elegant.

Janet caught her breath. His wife? Or fiancée? Perhaps a relative or friend? What did she know of Eden Varndell—except what she had been able to glean from magazines and newspapers in the past fortnight? His personal life was evidently taboo to a certain extent for there had never been any mention of a wife or fiancé ... just a resumé of his past work as a novelist, the mention of his lovely old house in Buckinghamshire, a few notes on his family— Janet remembered that there had been the mention of a sister.

Davina glanced at the girl curiously and paused as she reached her. 'Can I help you? Were you looking for someone?'

Janet blushed to the roots of her hair. 'I ... was just admiring the house,' she said—and knew how young, how naive, how foolish she must sound.

'Oh, I see.' One of Eden's fans, no doubt, she thought with amusement ... curious to see the house where he lives and writes his brilliant books. Or a guest in the village curious for a sight of the celebrity whose name was constantly being mentioned. She turned and looked at the house, endeavouring to see it through a stranger's eyes. 'It is rather lovely, isn't it?' She could not quite keep the pride and affection from her voice.

Janet looked at her quickly. 'Do you live here?' she asked impulsively, bluntly.

Davina raised an amused eyebrow. 'Well . . . yes, I do. I'm Davina Varndell.'

'Eden's sister . . .' Janet was covered in confusion as the words slipped out involuntarily.

Davina was intrigued. The girl had spoken as though she knew Eden personally and intimately . . . yet she was scarcely his type—so young, so immature, so easily embarrassed. She was remarkably pretty and Davina was struck by the amazing candour of lovely grey eyes—she could imagine that Eden might have taken a liking to this girl, after all.

'Yes,' she agreed easily. 'Eden's sister. Have we met? At a party, perhaps? I have a terrible memory for faces.'

'No . . .'

'Eden's at home if you want to see him,' she went on carelessly. 'You must forgive me for rushing off but I have an appointment.' She smiled and turned away.

Janet watched her walk down the slight incline of the road—and she knew that now she would have to call at the house. It was only too likely that Davina Varndell would tell her brother of the girl she had met at the gates, hovering uncertainly and obviously wanting to see him—she might describe her and Eden might guess immediately that it had been the girl he had met on a train—even if he could not remember her name.

Slowly, reluctantly, she approached the

97

house—just as a french window was pushed open at the side of the house and Eden Varndell stepped down into the garden, a cigarette in his hand and a certain weariness in his eyes.

A splash of bright colour caught his attention—and he turned indifferently to look at the girl in the orange dress who was about to climb the stone steps.

In a moment, he was running towards her. 'Janet!'

She turned, her eyes very bright. He remembered her—had recognised her instantly! She was no longer nervous and apprehensive ... merely a little shy as she met the warm delight in his dark eyes.

'Hallo ... I've brought your pencil back. I hope you don't mind?'

He was immediately checked by the easy, light tone of her voice. Fool that he was, he had almost caught her into his arms, so thrilled and glad to see her that all reason was cast to the winds. But her words brought him to his senses with a jerk.

'How nice to see you ... but you don't mean that you've come all this way for the sake of a pencil?' He smiled down at her youthful face, so dear to him, so well remembered.

'It was such a lovely day ... I was stifled in London. And I've been feeling rather guilty about the pencil ... I must have slipped it in my case without thinking. I should have sent it through the post straight away, I know—I expect you wondered what had happened to it.'

'I knew it was quite safe,' he assured her. 'This is really a delightful surprise! I've been trying to work without much success and I'm only too glad of an interruption. Come into the house and have some tea ... it's quite a walk from the station and it's a very hot day. Although you look remarkably cool—and very pretty.' He knew he was babbling but he simply could not stem the words. If he did not find release in talking he would be quite unable to resist the temptation to catch her to him and pour out his love and his longing.

'It's awful cheek to descend on you like this....'

'Of course it isn't! I'm glad you came—really glad. I told you that I hoped we'd be friends, Janet ... I hoped to hear from you ages ago.'

'I thought you might have forgotten all about me,' she said hesitantly.

He looked at her for a long moment. 'No ... I didn't forget you, Janet.' His voice was low and a little unsteady.

Within a few moments, it was a though the fortnight between had never been. They were at ease with each other, talking lightly over the tea-cups—and Janet was reminded forcibly of the hour they had spent in the buffet at Paddington. He took her over the house, showing her its hidden beauties, its many treasures with pride and affection. They wandered hand in hand about the rambling, well-kept grounds. They were young and in love and the world was a paradise created for them alone ... yet neither by word nor glance nor gesture did either of them betray the love that burned so brightly for each other. Janet was content with his liking, his warm welcome, the sense of mutual affinity, the friendship he openly offered ... she was conscious of being at peace for the first time in a fortnight and her singing heart did not urge to know that he loved her. She knew that it was not possible, might never be possible, but it was not a painful knowledge while she was with him and knew his warm friendliness.

Eden did not question her presence. Perhaps she had come on impulse. Perhaps she had thought about him more than he dared to hope. He could only be thankful that she had come, that she had not forgotten him, that he was granted these golden hours in her company ... and although he had not believed it possible he loved her more in these familiar and much-loved surroundings.

CHAPTER EIGHT

He paused to light a cigarette and Janet brushed a small fly from his cheek. He smiled at her ... and then the smile faded abruptly. He

100

caught the hand as she withdrew it and stared at the sapphire and diamond ring she was wearing. How had he failed to notice it before? A shadow passed across the glory of the day— and the agony that tore at his heart drove all the colour from his face.

With an effort he touched the ring with a careless gesture. 'So romance caught up with you, after all?' He was astonished to hear his own voice, even, light-hearted, betraying no more than casual interest.

A few days before the ring had weighed heavily on her hand and her heart. She had been conscious of it still as she journeyed to see the man she loved ... yet at the sight of him the ring and all it symbolised had fled from her mind. Dominic had been forgotten ... he had no place in this wonderful world that only held herself and Eden Varndell.

Now she was dismayed ... more than that, she knew a twisting of pain in her heart that he had shown so little concern. She could not expect him to dislike her engagement to another man yet his mild interest and light-hearted quip hurt her unbearably.

She turned away and twisted the ring on her finger. 'Yes ... it happens to us all, doesn't it?'

'Rather suddenly in some cases.' His tone was mocking and Janet uncomfortably remembered how quickly she had assured him that there were no complications in her life.

'It wasn't really ... sudden. I've known

Dominic for some months ... it was just that I didn't—expect him to be serious about me.'

'Does he know that you're here this afternoon?'

'Oh no! I mean ...' She broke off, confused. 'There was no need to tell him ... I only came because it was such a nice day. It was an impulse—I miss the country, you see. And I've been feeling guilty about your pencil—and the money I owed you.'

'I see.' He spoke grimly.

'Do you think I should have told him?' she asked anxiously.

He forced a laugh to his stiff lips. 'That depends on whether or not he's the jealous type.' He paused and went on: 'He might not believe in a platonic friendship.'

'Oh, I'm sure he does! He and Helen have been friends for ages—I told you about Helen, my room-mate. They're fond of each other but there's nothing silly about their friendship.' She spoke eagerly, hastily.

He nodded. 'Shall we go back to the house?'

She fell into step beside him, knowing that all the happiness and brightness of the day had vanished, conscious that he was angry with her for coming to see him when she was engaged to another man. But she had not come for any reason but to cement a friendship ... there could be no harm in that! Dominic had his own friends ... why couldn't she have friends, even men friends? Dominic had no need to be jealous ... she had promised to marry him, she wore his ring. Eden had no need to be angry ... it must be obvious that she had come out of friendship! She would not have had the courage to come if there was any fear that he would think she was chasing him!

'I must be getting back to town,' she said nervously. 'I really didn't mean to stay so long.'

'I'll drive you to the station.'

So he did not mean to detain her ... and her spirits sank even lower. Why had she come? Why had she followed that ridiculous impulse? Now everything was ruined. He would not want to see her again—ever! And now she had repaid him her fare and returned his pencil she would have no excuse for getting in touch with him.

'Thank you ... but I shall enjoy the walk.'

'I'd rather see you safely on to the train.'

She did not argue the point. There had been a note in his voice that did not brook further protest.

During the short run to the station, he talked almost without ceasing as though he feared to be silent. Janet made the effort to reply but she was feeling utterly miserable. She knew she would never see him again and she did not know what to do or to say. It seemed so strange. He had been so friendly, so nice—and then abruptly he had changed. The discovery that she was engaged to be married yet had

103

sought him out had evidently convinced him that it would not be wise to continue a friendship with her. She was surprised to learn that he was so narrow-minded. He could not know that she had fallen in love with him ... she had been so careful not to betray herself. Yet if he had guessed! It would explain his sudden decision to end a scarcely-begun friendship. No man would want to become involved with a girl who loved him while planning to marry someone else. Janet herself would be suspicious and contemptuous of any man who was guilty of the same thing.

She should never have promised to marry Dominic. It was not enough to be fond of him, to be afraid of hurting him. Sometimes it was kinder to be cruel when the happiness of two people was at stake.

She wanted to tell him that it was all a mistake—that she would not marry Dominic, after all. But she checked the impulse. Of what possible interest could it be to Eden? He would only be more convinced of her youth and silliness. And she would probably marry Dominic, anyway ... at least he loved and wanted her and would do his utmost to make her happy. At least she knew where she stood with Dominic ... he did not blow hot and cold like this man who puzzled her with his sudden changes of mood. At least she would not commit the absolute folly of breaking her engagement because she felt a passing attraction for another man—it *would* pass, she told herself firmly. Without encouragement it must surely die very quickly—and it was obvious that she was not going to get any encouragement from Eden himself!

'Your train is due in ten minutes.' He parked the car in the station forecourt and turned off the ignition.

'Thank you for making me so welcome ... you must have thought me an awful nuisance, intruding on your privacy, interrupting your work....'

'Of course I didn't. I was very glad to see you.'

'It's nice of you to say so.'

He managed to smile. 'I'm not just being polite. It was an afternoon to remember.'

Certainly he would never forget those few hours with the girl he loved. Golden, glorious hours that had etched themselves on his memory for ever. He was still stunned by the realisation that she meant to marry another man—and disappointed that she had wittingly deceived him about her feelings. It was as well to know where he stood but he could wish that she had been frank with him in the beginning. Then he would never have allowed himself to think about her, to dream about her, to fall in love with her. But he knew even as the thought touched his mind that it had been inevitable that he should love this girl—he had known at first sight that she was the only woman he would ever want—and now he knew that she was the one woman he simply could not have.

He had been determined to bid her goodbye and make an end to the acquaintance. It was pointless to torture himself by seeing her again, by falling deeper in love, by constantly reminding himself that she belonged to someone else. And yet now ... at the moment of parting, he could not allow her to walk out of his life so irrevocably.

He took her hand and held it firmly. 'Janet—I feel as though we've known each other always. We were never strangers ... I told you that last time we met, didn't I? You'll come and see me again?'

Her eyes brightened and her spirits rose with a leap. 'Oh yes ... if I may!'

'Whenever you wish ... friends don't need to wait for invitations. I shall always be pleased to see you—at any time. But ... don't come if it will make difficulties for you with your fiancé, Janet,' he added firmly. 'I doubt very much if he'd approve—I don't suppose I would approve in similar circumstances.'

'Dominic won't mind,' she told him eagerly. 'I'll tell him that we are friends ... he'll understand.'

Eden's glance was sceptical. 'You know the man—I don't.'

'You'd like him,' she said slowly.

'Yes, I expect I would,' he lied, knowing a fierce and jealous hatred of this unknown

Dominic. 'When are you getting married?'

'I . . . I don't know—fairly soon, I think. He doesn't want to wait.'

'You'll give up nursing, of course?'

She nodded ruefully. 'It's a hospital rule that they don't employ married nurses. I shall miss it all so much.'

He was puzzled. She did not seem as pleased with the prospect of marriage as one would expect of a newly-engaged girl. Did nursing mean more to her than the man she planned to marry? For the thousandth time he realised the many drawbacks to loving a girl he scarcely knew. How could he gauge how deeply involved her emotions were where this man was concerned? How could he guess at the circumstances which led her into an engagement so abruptly when only a fortnight ago she had seemed completely heartwhole? How could he know whether or not she was telling the truth at any time?

'Then I'll see you again?'

'Yes, of course.' Her smile was warm and eager.

He released the slim fingers which had been lying so calmly and naturally in his clasp. She opened the car door and stepped out on the forecourt. His sudden change of mood and the realisation that he wanted to see her again had filled her with joyful content. She could leave him now without an aching heart and a despairing spirit.

Her train was approaching the station and with a hurried word and a hasty wave she was gone ... and Eden sat in his car outside the station long after the train was out of sight.

It might have been better if she had never come to Raisney St. Mary that day. Better by far to love a memory than to know that the reality was out of his reach. But he had the promise of her friendship, the promise that she would come again—and he could only hope that something, anything, would prevent her marriage to the unknown Dominic...

Janet sat in the compartment of the train that carried her back to London and thought about Eden.

He was just as she had remembered—and so much dearer to her for the hours she had spent with him. It seemed so wrong that she should be contemplating a future with Dominic when every part of her being longed for Eden. Everything fell into place when she was with him ... the sun seemed to shine for them alone, the bright colours of the flowers, the green of the grass and the trees, the high, sweet song of the birds seemed to have been created for them alone. She had been conscious of perfect contentment as they strolled hand in hand through those lovely grounds—she had known in her heart that he was contented and happy to be with her, too.

Now she felt as though a vital part of her was missing. She was no longer whole and life no

108

longer had any purpose.

Janet had never realised how demanding, all-embracing love could be but she did not doubt for a moment that she loved and needed Eden more than anything else in the world. How could she marry Dominic, feeling as she did? He would not hold her to their engagement—and she would be free again, free to love Eden, free to hope for his love in time.

Yet she had no reason to believe that his interest held anything more than liking and a desire for friendship. He had not been dismayed by her engagement. He had not thought it strange that she should visit him although she was engaged to Dominic. He had not given any sign that Janet meant anything to him but a new friend in whom he was naturally interested. She was not to see him again except of her own seeking when she would be 'always welcome'. As a friend—no more.

He would be pleased to see her again—but he did not expect to do so and Janet knew that without being told. He thought that Dominic would disapprove. He believed her visit that day had been motivated by impulse and would never be repeated. He suspected that once she was involved with plans for her wedding she would forget all about a man she had met only twice.

That was how it would be in many cases. But she loved Eden and she could not dismiss him from her life. She had to see him again. She had to hold him to that promise of friendship. The occasional meeting might keep her love alive and emphasise that she loved in vain ... it would also keep her in touch with him and that was very important to her.

If only Dominic had not fallen in love with her and asked her to marry him. If only she had not been so miserable about Eden and so afraid of hurting Dominic that she had agreed almost without realising it. If only Eden loved her as she loved him—and had allowed her to know it.

She would break her engagement immediately. She would hurt Dominic but he would understand and accept her love for someone else ... and then she thought of how she would feel if she discovered that Eden was planning to be married and her heart shrank from inflicting such agony on Dominic who had done nothing to deserve it.

Perhaps she should say nothing for a little while. Perhaps Dominic would change his mind. She would talk him out of an early wedding on the plea that she wanted to nurse for a few more months. Anything could happen in that time—particularly if she continued to see Eden from time to time. She might cease to love him ... although she knew that was impossible. Eden might come to love her ... although she doubted that so much joy would ever be her lot in life. Dominic might find someone else...

Her thoughts snatched eagerly at that last hope. Helen! Dominic had cared for her once ... why else had he wanted to marry her. And Helen was only drifting in her engagement to Adrian Hart ... it was an odd affair and already there were signs that it would end eventually. Perhaps Helen was more fond of Dominic than she realised—and that would solve everything beautifully!

Except that things could not be arranged so neatly and satisfactorily in real life as in romantic novels!

Except that the securing of mutual happiness for Dominic and Helen would not solve her own problem, would not secure Eden's love for herself or ensure her future as his wife!

It was all too difficult and her head was beginning to ache and her heart was heavy ... and they were drawing into Victoria and she must make sure that her ticket was safe...

Davina met her brother again at dinner that evening. 'Did you have a visitor this afternoon?' she asked as she took her place at the table.

'A visitor?'

'Mm ... a girl. She was by the gate when I went out—and it struck me that she couldn't make up her mind whether or not to come up to the house.'

'Oh ... yes. It was Janet.'

'I thought it might be.' Her voice was warm with pleasure. 'So you were making yourself miserable for nothing. She did get in touch with you, after all.'

'She came to tell me that she is engaged to be married,' he said curtly.

'Nice of her! Couldn't she have told you in a letter? Did she have to come here and raise your hopes? I thought she looked a nice girl but I've certainly changed my mind about her now!'

'She is a nice girl . . . that's why she wouldn't hide behind a letter. I admire her for coming.'

Davina looked at him curiously. 'Well, you *must* have worn your heart on your sleeve on that wretched train, darling! I didn't think you could be so impetuous.'

'Don't be ridiculous! Janet hasn't a clue as to the way I feel about her . . . she's a sweet child who came to see me on impulse. The fact of her engagement came out in conversation.'

'Why should she want to see you if she's engaged to someone else?' she asked bluntly.

He shrugged. 'How do I know? She likes me, I guess . . . people do, you know. Anyway, she wanted to return my silver pencil—she borrowed it on the train and forgot to give it back to me.'

'The excuse served its purpose,' she said drily.

'She didn't need an excuse . . . I'd already made it obvious that I'd like to meet her again.'

She leaned forward with warm sympathy in her eyes. 'And how do you feel now, Eden? Are you still crazy about her? Or have you come to your senses now that you've seen her again?'

'I'm in love with her.' His tone was firm, almost defiant.

'Well, you should know how you feel. You're not a child, darling. I'm sorry ... I wish things had been different for you, Eden.'

He pushed away his untouched plate and rose to his feet. 'Sorry ... I just can't face it. I'll be in the study if you want me for anything.'

Davina meant well. She was genuinely fond of him and concerned for his happiness. But he felt that he could not endure her anxious questions, her obvious sympathy, her ill-concealed astonishment any longer.

Of course she was surprised that he should fall so heavily in love at his age—and with a girl so different to the women he had known in the past. Her sympathy was facile because Davina's own emotions had never been stirred to such heights and she could not imagine or credit the way he was feeling.

He knew that living with him had not been easy for Davina during the last fortnight. He found it difficult to live with himself.

But it was all so hopeless. He felt ten times worse now that he had seen Janet again ... before he could always hope that she would get in touch with him, that a friendship might be possible, that one day she might come to love him in return. Now he knew that she was in love with another man and planning to marry him—and that there was no hope in his heart, no foundation for his foolish dreams, no comfort in the long, lonely years that stretched before him.

He should not have urged Janet to keep in touch with him. He should have let her walk out of his life—the emptiness would have been easier to bear than the thought of occasional meetings which would only serve to emphasise the futility of his love and the finality of her marriage to someone else...

CHAPTER NINE

The *Coq d'Honneur* was a pleasant, intimate little restaurant just off Piccadilly. It was one of Dominic's favourite haunts these days although at one time he had scarcely liked the place. Helen had always liked it and they had used it frequently in the past. Perhaps that explained the restaurant's present attraction for him...

Certainly he found that he went there on many occasions when he was at a loose end. This evening, for instance. Janet had pleaded a lecture and the necessity to wash her hair and he had not been displeased with the thought of an evening to himself. Matters were very strained between them and Dominic blamed himself. It was difficult to play the part of an ardent lover without giving cause for suspicion and he could not help feeling that Janet sensed his lack of ardour, his struggle with his emotions and felt that she was failing him in some way.

Poor little Janet. He knew that she was not happy. She tried too hard to be natural and gay in his company, to ignore the gulf that seemed to be widening between them. She was very much in his thoughts this evening but they were not pleasant or welcome thoughts. He felt that he could not go on with their engagement. It was not fair to Janet to allow her to believe that he loved her, that he was impatient to marry her. It was not her fault that she had failed to stir him to emotion. It was not her fault that he did not wish to marry her.

The woman he wanted was out of his reach. He could surely find a measure of happiness with Janet and her happiness must be sufficient reward for the sacrifice. And it would be a sacrifice. He had always cherished his freedom and his independence and his ideal of the perfect wife. Rather than take second-best he had been prepared to go his solitary way for the rest of his life. But Janet loved him and that complicated matters.

He could think of no real reason not to marry her—except that he loved someone else. No doubt Janet would make a comfortable and pleasing wife and perhaps in time he would learn to love her sufficiently to forget his dream of the unattainable.

He reached a decision. He would marry Janet—he would not back out of their engagement—and to hell with his doubts and fears!

He stood at the bar, a tall, handsome man with a troubled look in his eyes. Oblivious to curious glances, he had been too preoccupied to notice the other occupants of the bar. But now, dismissing his problems, he turned and looked about him, half-consciously hoping to see an acquaintance. He did not want to be alone this evening, after all. He was tired of circling the familiar problem in his mind.

He stiffened and a little of the colour receded from his cheeks. He wondered how long Helen had been sitting at that corner table and wondered why she had not approached him. It was odd that she should be on her own.

She was a striking figure in a black cocktail dress, her auburn hair piled high on her head. He admired her cool self-possession and the air of sophistication. She was a beautiful woman ... much too beautiful, much too good for that damned playwright who had trampled on too many women in the past. He was forcibly reminded of the last time he had brought Helen to this restaurant—the night when he had told her that she would marry him one day and watched the fierce brightness of anger touch her eyes. He had been much too sure of himself—and of her. Now he could understand her anger. At the time it had merely amused him without pricking the bubble of arrogant conceit and confidence.

Time had proved him wrong. She meant to marry Hart—if and when the man ever agreed to a wedding date. He must be a fool not to appreciate his good fortune, to think he could keep Helen dangling indefinitely, to even want to delay their marriage. But she did not seem to mind unduly. Evidently she loved enough to forgive Hart's insulting reluctance.

Helen did not glance his way. Her eyes did not leave the glass-paned doors of the bar—and Dominic realised that she was waiting for someone and gradually losing patience. There was a tautness about the lovely curve of her mouth and a gleam of annoyance in those violet eyes. Her fingers toyed irritably with a cigarette that she had not yet bothered to light.

Dominic walked over to her table and produced his lighter. 'Would madam like a light?'

She glanced up absently. The she recognised him. 'Oh ... Dominic, what are you doing here?'

She bent her head over the flame of his lighter and he noticed the lovely sweep of her neck and longed to press his lips to the tiny tendrils that curled on her nape.

'Having a drink. Very shortly I shall be

having a meal.'

Her gaze went past him to the door. 'Ask a silly question.'

'May I get you a drink?'

'Thank you.'

He realised that she was scarcely aware of him and anger wrenched in him briefly. He took her glass and strode to the bar. But by the time he returned to her table he had mastered his annoyance and reminded himself that he had no claim to her attention or interest other than the demands of mere courtesy. They had seen very little of each other in recent months—and there had seemed to be very little to say to each other when they did meet. But things had been different a few weeks ago— when he had met her outside the Nurses Home and invited her to go with him to Paddington. For that short period of time, she had seemed to be in sympathy with him and he had valued her warmth and friendliness.

Helen glanced at her watch and bit her lip. She said coldly: 'I imagine that, vulgarly speaking, I've been stood up.'

He sat down and pushed her drink towards her. 'I expect it was unavoidable, Helen. No man in his right senses would fail to keep an appointment with you, my dear.'

She gestured impatiently. 'Don't be so smooth, Dominic. It's very irritating. Compliments from you are much too rare to be sincere!'

118

'On the contrary,' he said quietly. 'You should always distrust a man who is too lavish with his compliments. Mine are rare—but always sincere.'

Helen looked at him thoughtfully. Then the annoyance faded from her eyes, her mouth relaxed and she smiled at him. 'Sorry ... I shouldn't vent my spleen on you, Dominic.'

'I'm always on call—whatever you require of me,' he told her swiftly, disarmingly. 'It isn't the first time I've been a whipping-boy.'

She laughed reluctantly. 'You've changed,' she said abruptly.

He looked alarmed. 'Have I? In what way?'

She cradled her chin in her hand and looked up at him with amusement in her eyes. 'I don't really know ... you're more human, I think.'

'Oh, I've always been human,' he protested.

'No ... you were always too busy keeping everyone at a distance,' she told him calmly. 'Janet has been good for you, Dominic.'

His eyes narrowed. 'Do you think so?'

'Certainly. Are you really going to marry her?'

'Isn't that rather a personal question?'

'I suppose so ... but we've known each other too long to stand on ceremony, surely?'

He played for time by reaching for his cigarette case, carefully extracting a cigarette, fumbling with his lighter.

Helen watched him curiously. 'That isn't like you,' she told him directly. He glanced at her with a question in his eyes. 'Fiddling with a lighter, I mean. You're always so economic with your hands.'

'I'm a surgeon,' he retorted coolly and drew deeply on his cigarette.

'Exactly. You're too well trained to fumble—so I must have disconcerted you for the moment. Isn't it settled, Dominic? I've thought that Janet has been acting very oddly since you became engaged—but I couldn't be sure if that was your fault ... or someone else's!'

'My dear Helen! I'm afraid I don't understand your riddles!'

'You forget that I was with you at Paddington,' she reminded him quietly. 'Did Janet ever mention...'

He cut her short with an edge to his voice: 'I'm afraid you leaped to conclusions that day, Helen. Janet cares for me too much to be interested in other men.'

'That should please you,' she said drily. 'But I don't think it does. Don't you love Janet? Don't you want to marry her? You forget that I know you very well—and it's obvious that the very mention of Janet puts you in a cleft spin.'

'You said that I'd changed,' he said curtly. 'I don't think you know the new Dominic at all, Helen.'

'Perhaps you're right.' It was obvious that he did not wish to talk about Janet.

It seemed ironic that this new, more human,

120

more appealing Dominic should no longer be her concern. She was going to marry Adrian ... and the man who had once proposed so coolly, had been arrogant, presumptuous, insufferable. But Dominic had lost a lot of his arrogance and there was a warmth and an appeal that had been lacking in the old days.

His friendship with Janet had melted the icy indifference. It was odd that Janet should seem so unhappy since she wore Dominic's beautiful ring ... if she loved him then she should be dancing on air! Helen suspected that her friend was not sure of her feelings and it was obvious that Dominic was trying to understand and forgive the change of heart. Yet they had only recently become engaged! Was Janet afraid to be honest with Dominic ... or had he swept her into an engagement, afraid to lose her, convincing her that she would soon forget the man who had caused her to have doubts about her love for him.

She decided that she had misinterpreted the tone of his voice when he claimed that Janet cared too much to be interested in anyone else. It had really been a note of bravado, a desperate attempt to convince himself, and she had been foolish to believe that he sounded rather rueful. In any case, it would not be fair to turn the knife in the wound by talking of Janet and his affairs.

'This is really too bad of Adrian,' she said easily. 'And it's a frightful blow to my vanity.'

He had guessed that she was waiting for Adrian Hart. For the thousandth time, he wondered what she saw in the man—a notorious rake, unscrupulous and cynical, the type who would plunge into any sordid business solely to alleviate boredom. Helen seemed an odd choice of wife for such a man but no doubt she seemed refreshingly different to the women he had known in his life.

'Is he very late?'

'Almost an hour ... he won't come now, of course.'

'I expect he would be surprised to know that you waited so long for him.'

'No ... not Adrian.' There was faint cynicism in her voice. 'He would be furious if he arrived two hours late to find I hadn't waited for him.' She smiled. 'I've changed too ... once I wouldn't have waited more than ten minutes for any man.'

'Hart seems to hold you in complete thrall,' he said stiffly.

Amusement lurked about her lips. 'You detest him, don't you?'

Dominic shrugged. 'I scarcely know the man.'

'The arrogance is creeping back,' Helen teased him mischievously. 'I know you don't like him ... you betray it so easily. You always speak of him as *"Hart"* or *"the man"*—and your voice has icicles a foot long.'

'I imagine that my liking has little or nothing

to say in the matter,' he pointed out quietly.

'Of course it hasn't ... but I find it rather amusing. You see, Adrian is extremely hostile to you—yet, as you pointed out, you scarcely know each other.'

'No doubt you told him that I wanted to marry you at one time,' he said wearily.

She stared at him. 'Yes ... I did. How could you know?'

'You're a woman,' he said lightly. 'And women can never resist parading their former conquests. In the circumstances, it isn't surprising that Hart views me with hostility. I shall always be a potential rival in his eyes.'

'You were never a conquest,' she said quickly. 'You merely wanted a convenient marriage—a suitable wife.' She invested the words with a wealth of contempt.

'True,' he agreed quietly. 'And I've learned to agree with your claim that my proposal was an insult.'

'You *have* changed!' she exclaimed, laughing. 'Whereas I no longer think it *was* an insult, Dominic. In a way, it was rather a compliment. You're probably the only man who has ever believed that I'd be a good wife to have around!'

'You're forgetting Hart,' he reminded her smoothly.

'Oh, Adrian doesn't expect me to be a good wife—and he knows that I'm certainly not a suitable wife for a playwright. At the moment,

I make allowances for his work because I'm not too sure of my ground ... but I shall be a very demanding wife.'

'A very selfish one, it seems.'

She wrinkled her nose at him. 'Don't you think I've had enough of the theatre in my life, Dominic?'

'If *you* think so then you shouldn't consider marrying a man so closely connected with the theatre,' he told her abruptly.

She widened her eyes. 'But Adrian wants to marry me,' she said with an assumption of innocence.

'Apparently Hart's wishes are all that matter,' he said coldly.

She relented swiftly. 'I'm a beast to tease you, Dominic.' She hesitated a moment and then she said: 'I do wonder sometimes if I'm doing the sensible thing, you know. Adrian can be very difficult—and I'm not the most patient or understanding of women.'

He caught her hand. 'Then don't marry him.' It was an effort to keep the urgency out of his voice, to speak lightly, almost indifferently.

She was silent, her eyes meeting his with a steady gaze. Then gently she withdrew her hand from his clasp. It was good to know that he cared enough to try to persuade her from making what might be a disastrous step ... but it would be absolute folly to imagine that anything but the genuine interest of friendship lay behind his words.

'I seem to be talking a great deal of nonsense,' she said airily. 'Probably because I'm so hungry—and I've had a drink too many on an empty stomach.'

'Dine with me,' he invited swiftly.

She laughed into his eyes. 'I've no intention of saying no, Dominic. Don't you know enough about women to recognise an angle for an invitation?'

'I've learned not to take too much for granted,' he returned easily.

'You have been learning your lessons well,' she teased lightly. Then as she rose to her feet, she slipped her hand into his arm and said warmly: 'I *am* glad you chanced to be here tonight, Dominic ... I hate being left in the lurch.'

The words hurt although he realised that she meant them entirely on their face value. He should be grateful for that sudden warmth, the impulsive gesture of her hand on his arm—and there was no point in looking a gift horse in the mouth. She was with him ... he would ensure that the evening did not break up too soon ... what did it matter that she thought of him merely as a stopgap for Adrian Hart? The man's default had brought him an unexpected gift—and he would use it to advantage.

He had reason to regret the faint, unmistakable hostility of the past months ... and this was his opportunity to make amends for his clumsiness and to ensure that their friendship was renewed on a firmer footing.

Neither Janet nor Adrian Hart were mentioned again that evening. They contented themselves with talking of former evenings spent together, of mutual friends, of St. Cecilia's, of current films and concerts, of books and music and art.

Those few hours spent with Helen were like a long, cool glass of water to a man who had walked for days in an arid desert. He knew that he had missed her friendship, her affection, even their silly quarrels that had stemmed from trivialities and been speedily forgotten. He knew that he loved her ... that he had always loved her ... that he would always love her whole-heartedly. He knew that he had been blind and clumsy and stupid—that he had only himself to blame for the fact that she was planning to marry Hart and that he was engaged to Janet. It was too late to mend matters ... but her friendship would be very dear to him.

Helen was furious with Adrian but, after those first moments, she realised the futility of betraying her anger. It was easier and more pleasant to treat the matter lightly. She did not want Dominic's sympathy or his advice. He was certainly excellent company. She could not remember when she had enjoyed herself so much as on this evening.

Dominic's company more than compensated for Adrian's default ... but her pleasure in the evening did not make her feel more tolerant of the excuses that Adrian would certainly offer when she saw or heard from him again.

It was really surprising that Dominic had altered so much. She had always been fond of him despite the annoying traits in his character. Now those traits seemed to have disappeared ... or perhaps she was viewing him with more tolerant eyes.

Her heart went out to him as she thought of his anxiety over Janet. He tried so hard to conceal his hurt—and a less perceptive woman might have been deceived. But Helen knew that he was hurt and troubled ... and she wished she could help him in some way. She could not resolve his affairs for him. She could not talk to Janet like a maiden aunt and make her realise what she would be throwing away if she decided not to marry Dominic. She could only show her affection and her sympathy as plainly as she dared. She could only strive to make him forget, if only for a few hours, the heartache that Janet had caused.

So she was her very sweetest self, animated and warm-hearted, generous with her approval, teasing him, reminding him of amusing incidents in the past, encouraging him to talk of his work and his dreams ... quite unaware that every word, every gesture, every glance only endeared her to him all the more. But he perfectly understood her motives and wished he could assure her that her sympathy was wasted, that far from being hurt by a reluctance on Janet's part to marry him he was being swept along by a tidal wave into a marriage he did not want nor welcome...

CHAPTER TEN

Janet's engagement to the S.S.O. had not been publicly announced yet the grapevine had garnered the knowledge in some strange way and she inevitably met with some teasing.

Escaping from a group of students who had surrounded her on her way across the small park that separated the main buildings of St. Cecilia's from the minor clinics and the Medical School and the Nurses Hostel, Janet almost collided with Martin Grey. Still flushed and embarrassed, she was conscious of a feeling of dismay. She had been avoiding Martin of late because of an unaccountable sense of guilt and she was not very pleased to run into him now.

He paused and looked down at her steadily. 'Hallo, Janet. You're quite a stranger these days.'

She could not pass him with a careless word. He had been too good a friend in the early days and the thought of him could still bring a surge of warm affection.

'Hallo, Martin ... where have you been hiding?' she countered with an attempt at lightness.

'I've been around,' he assured her. 'Are you in a hurry—or have you time to sit and have a cigarette with me?'

'I'm off duty now,' she admitted. She walked with him to a nearby bench and accepted the cigarette he offered.

'I gather that congratulations are in order.'

She looked down at the glowing end of her cigarette. 'Oh ... you've heard?'

'Of course ... it's the talk of the hospital—or didn't you know? It isn't every day that a nurse hooks a senior surgeon.'

'Don't Martin!' she protested involuntarily. 'It ... it wasn't like that!'

He relented, noting the suspicious brightness of her eyes. 'Sorry ... I suppose I'm a bit jealous. You may remember that I was pretty keen on you myself at one time.'

'Yes.' Her voice was low. 'But it was never very serious.'

'I couldn't afford it to be,' he retorted grimly. 'But I was fond of you—still am, for that matter. I can't say I'm delighted to hear your news because I'm not—oh, I've nothing against Hammond. But Hammond and you—no, Janet, that I can't stomach!'

'I don't see why not,' she said indignantly.

'Listen, sweetie—without being rude, you just aren't his type, you know. My type ... yes.

But Hammond—he's never run around with nurses in the past. Why now—and why you?'

'Why not?' The heat of anger was in her cheeks now.

'Hell ... I'm making a thorough mess of this,' he said helplessly. 'Look, be reasonable, Jan! Doesn't it seem odd that he should suddenly ignore all the rules and decide to marry a nurse half his age and with whom he has nothing in common?'

Janet rose abruptly. She threw her cigarette to the ground and stamped on it. 'You can't expect me to agree with you!'

'I expect you to face facts! Seriously, Jan, is it credible?'

'Of course it is! There's such a thing as love, you know—or perhaps you don't! People like you always try to be clever, to explain it away as a biological urge—but it exists ... and it doesn't bother about rules or ages or anything else! In any case, how can you possibly know whether or not Dominic and I have anything in common?'

He shrugged. 'I know you, Jan—and I know enough of Dominic Hammond to believe that if love comes into it at all, it's pretty one-sided. The man hasn't an ounce of emotion in him— and it's my guess that you're just bowled over because he's an important man and he's taken some sort of liking to you.'

'You seem to have forgotten that he means to marry me,' she told him tartly.

130

'I'll believe that when he puts a wedding ring on your finger,' he retorted.

'I don't have to discuss my affairs with you!'

Janet marched away from him with her chin high and her eyes blazing with anger. Martin stood undecided for a moment, then he hurried to catch her arm.

'Janet ... I've bungled the whole thing. I didn't mean to make you angry ... I just wanted to warn you!'

She stared at him, bewildered. 'Warn me? What about?'

'About Hammond. I'm pretty fond of you sweetie—I don't want you to get hurt. Don't trust a man like him—you'll get hurt in the long run.' There was concern and affection in his eyes as he looked down at her. Then he dropped her arm, swung on his heel and strode away.

Janet ran after him. 'Martin!'

He turned. 'What is it?'

'What made you say a thing like that?' she demanded. 'Why shouldn't I trust Dominic? Do you know something about him that I should know?'

He hesitated, reluctant to hurt her, convinced that she was deeply in love with the surgeon. 'I guess it was nothing,' he said awkwardly.

Exasperated, she could have shaken him. 'What was nothing? What are you trying to tell me?'

131

'Only that I saw him the other night in the West End ... don't press me, Janet—it isn't my business!'

'You should have thought of that before,' she said tartly. 'You saw Dominic ... with a woman, do you mean?'

He nodded. 'I thought they seemed pretty friendly.'

The brightness of hope gleamed in her eyes and her spirits soared. Oh, if it was only true ... if only she could believe that Dominic had found someone else, that she might be released from an engagement which was proving to be a spiritual bondage.

'I suppose you didn't know the woman?'

He thrust his hands in his pockets. 'It was Helen.'

Abruptly those soaring spirits plummeted ... Helen, only Helen. They had been friends too long for Janet to believe that escape lay in their obviously chance meeting in the West End.

He looked anxiously at those dark eyes, so dark with pain, and the sudden tremulous drooping of her lips. 'I'm sorry, Jan ...'

'Oh, don't be so silly!' she snapped ... and ran from him, on the verge of tears.

Instinctively she put a hand to her throat where Dominic's ring lay on a slender chain about her neck for nurses were not allowed to wear any jewellery on duty. That ring had brought her nothing but unhappiness.

132

She scarcely knew how their engagement had come about. Fool that she was, her thoughts had been miles away—with Eden. Dominic had said something to her that barely impinged itself on her conscious mind and she had murmured a vague affirmative. When he slipped the heavy ring on her finger she had realised that she had committed herself to marrying him in that moment ... and she had been so startled, so dismayed, that she had not been able to think of any escape from an engagement she did not welcome.

She knew that it was weak and foolish to allow Dominic to believe that she meant to marry him ... but it was the weakness and folly that stemmed from kindness of heart. She was fond of Dominic ... fond enough to realise how easy it had been to imagine herself in love with him ... too fond to think lightly of hurting him. Perhaps he would realise one day that she did not love him. It seemed incredible now that he could be deceived by her feeble pretence of ardour and enthusiasm. Surely he must sense her reluctance to discuss wedding plans, to talk of their future together, to be alone with him more than was inevitable. Didn't he wonder why she should suddenly desire the bright lights—visits to the theatre, parties, nightclubs—or did he merely assume that she was enjoying the novelty of these things and liked the escort of a man who knew his way about Town? He fell in with her suggestions, seemed perfectly willing to take her wherever she wished to go and did not seem to mind that they were seldom on their own these days.

Janet did not really enjoy the gay life. But it was an avenue of escape from intimate tête-à-têtes and it also offered the possibility that she might see Eden at a theatre or a nightclub or a party. As a successful writer it was likely that he had a full social life and the hope of running into him by chance outweighed the fear that she might see him in the company of another woman.

He was constantly in her thoughts but so far she had not plucked up enough courage to get in touch with him again. It would be too humiliating if he were to guess that her interest stemmed from more than friendly motives. In any case, pride forbade her to write or telephone when he made no attempt to see her again. It seemed so strange when she remembered his warm greeting, his kindness, the easy affinity they had shared on that memorable afternoon at his home. No doubt the news of her engagement had been a sufficient check even if he had ever entertained the thought that their friendship might develop into something warmer in time.

Helen was in their room, carefully painting her nails, when Janet went in. She glanced up with a smile. 'Hallo ... are you off duty already? I didn't realise it was so late.'

'I thought you were going out,' Janet said in

surprise for it was Helen's free day and she had not expected to see her in the room.

She shrugged. 'Adrian phoned to say that he's unexpectedly tied up. He's going to call again when he can get away.'

'So you're left to kick your heels!' Janet spoke with the heat of indignation for she could not understand that Helen seemed indifferent to Adrian Hart's cavalier treatment.

'Oh, I had several things to do,' she returned airily.

Janet sat on the edge of her bed. 'I think you're crazy!' she said bluntly.

Helen raised a cool eyebrow. 'Do you?'

'I wouldn't sit about waiting for any man to call me at his pleasure! He treats you like a doormat, Helen—and you don't even mind, apparently!'

'Oh, I mind ... but there isn't much I can do about it, is there?'

'Not if you love him, I suppose,' she replied soberly.

'Do you doubt it?'

Janet hesitated. 'Sometimes,' she said eventually.

Helen smiled, intently studying her varnished nails.

'When you go out with other men, for instance.'

Helen's eyes narrowed abruptly. 'What on earth do you mean?'

Janet went to the dressing-table, took off her

135

cap and ran a comb through her short, fair curls. 'I wish you'd told me that you were with Dominic the other night.'

'Dominic!' Helen laughed lightly. 'Don't be silly, ducky! I wouldn't dream of poaching on your preserves.'

'I know that—but other people don't and you know how they delight in making mountains out of molehills,' she said lightly.

'But I haven't been out with Dominic in months!'

Hurt by the blatant lie, Janet swung to face her friend. 'You were seen!'

Helen frowned. 'It seems to me that someone is trying to make mischief ... who told you that I went out with Dominic?'

'That doesn't matter! You were seen with him in the West End the other night. Oh, I'm not jealous—I'm not so silly. But it does seem odd that neither you nor Dominic bothered to mention it to me. Did you really think I'd object?'

Helen's brow cleared suddenly. 'Now I know what you're talking about! I ran into Dominic at the *Coq d'Honneur* and we had dinner together. He was on his own and I had arranged to meet Adrian there but he didn't turn up. Dominic took pity on me and fed me—that's all there was to it! I didn't mention it because I didn't particularly want you to know that Adrian failed to keep a date with me—and I expect Dominic forgot about it because it was such a trivial encounter.'

'I didn't think it was anything else,' Janet protested, startled by the defiance in Helen's tone. 'I suppose I was just annoyed because Mart . . . because I was told that you'd been out together and yet neither of you mentioned it.'

'I'll have something to say to Martin Grey if he tries to stir up trouble between you and Dominic!' Helen said tartly. 'He's half in love with you himself but he's always loved his freedom too much to do anything about it! He's just jealous, Janet . . . don't pay too much attention to anything he says! You don't have to worry about Dominic—or me, for that matter. I'm in love with Adrian and you needn't doubt that at any time. As for Dominic—well, the sun shines from your eyes where he's concerned and it's my opinion that you're making him thoroughly miserable!'

'*I am?*'

'Well, of course you are! You're always making piffling excuses not to see him! You won't set a definite date for getting married! And you drag him all over London rather than spend an evening alone with him in case he tries to pin you down to a date!'

Janet gestured helplessly, completely taken aback by Helen's accusations. 'Is that what he told you?'

'Of course not! Dominic isn't the type to criticise the woman he loves to another woman. But I know that he has something on

137

his mind—and it can only be you! And I know you pretty well by now, Janet—and it's pretty obvious that you can't make up your mind whether or not you want to marry Dominic. You're just one of those people who want the moon until it's in their hand—and then they just don't know what to do with it!'

'Is that really how I seem to you?' Her voice was low, tremulous. She was shocked to realise how thinly she had veiled her reluctance to marry Dominic ... and terrified that Dominic might also have seen through the pretence and be as miserable as Helen claimed. She did not want him to be hurt, to be unhappy...

Helen swiftly reined the anger that had threatened to run away with her. All the indignation in the world would not help Dominic if she convinced Janet that she had made a mistake. That was not her intention.

She said quietly, more kindly: 'I'm sorry, Jan—I didn't mean to fly off the handle. But I've known Dominic a long time and I know that he was very badly hurt once—I wouldn't want it to happen again. I expect he's told you about it?'

'No ... how was he hurt?'

'Oh, it's not important now. It happened years ago—some girl who turned him down.'

'You?' she asked shrewdly.

Helen stared in amazement. 'Me? Heavens, no! Dominic was never in love with me, ducky—and I expect he thanks his lucky stars

138

these days that I didn't agree to marry him.'

'Why didn't you?'

'Obvious ... I didn't love him and I wasn't prepared to marry a man who merely wanted a suitable wife and thought I'd fit the bill. But we're not discussing Dominic and me! What's wrong, Janet? I thought you really cared for him—yet since you've been engaged you've been acting so oddly. Have you changed your mind?'

She sat down, her hands tightly clasped in her lap. 'I ... I don't know.'

'Is it just nerves—or is there someone else?'

'Nerves, I expect.' She forced a little laugh.

'You're really very lucky, Janet—Dominic is a wonderful person and he'll make a marvellous husband,' Helen said gently.

'Yes, I know ... it's just that—Helen, do you really think I'm the right type for him? I just can't see myself as his wife.'

'That is nerves and nothing else!' she stated firmly. 'What has type got to do with it? Dominic loves you ... and you love him, don't you?'

'Yes ... I suppose so,' she said lamely. Was it possible that she did love him and that this confusion of her emotions was born of a mere physical attraction for another man?

'Of course you do! I haven't known you all these months without knowing the way you feel about Dominic! He loves you ... he wants to marry you—what more do you want? A few months ago you couldn't think of anything else!'

'That's true. . . .'

'The best thing you can do is to marry Dominic as soon as possible. Then you'll wonder what on earth you were worrying about.'

'I rather wanted to go on nursing for a while. . . .'

'Nonsense! You've lost all your interest in nursing and everyone knows it. It's quite natural. What you really want is to get married and have a couple of babies—and I just can't imagine why you're dithering so much.'

It was true that her interest in nursing had waned considerably during recent weeks but she could scarcely tell Helen that her thoughts had been of Eden Varndell rather than a future spent with Dominic. She could never admit that she had become engaged to one man while loving another with every ounce of her being. She could never admit that she had encouraged Dominic to believe that she loved him and wanted to marry him while seeking an avenue of escape from an unwelcome engagement. She could never admit that she was such a fool as to fall in love with a man she barely knew, someone who was not really interested in her, while a man like Dominic was hers for the claiming.

Helen must be right, of course. She should marry Dominic and then perhaps she could forget the man who was rapidly becoming an obsession. She had once believed that she loved Dominic therefore it was only logical to assume that he was a man she could love ... perhaps in time she could recapture the old feeling and meanwhile give him the happiness he wanted and needed so much.

CHAPTER ELEVEN

Helen toyed with a cigarette, staring at the untouched coffee on the table before her. She scarcely heard the music that filled the room, so deep in thought was she—and Adrian at the piano, with his back to her, was too absorbed in the music to wonder at her long silence.

She had always despised those people whose only interest in life seemed to be the interference in the affairs of others and she had not enjoyed laying down the law to Janet. Her only comfort, if comfort it was, was the knowledge that she had ensured Dominic's happiness for a date had been fixed for the wedding and Janet had already given her notice to Matron.

She wondered why the news had brought her so little pleasure. She should be delighted that her lecture had brought such rapid results. She should be gratified that she had paved the way for Dominic's peace of mind. She should be satisfied to know that Janet seemed much happier now that everything was settled.

It had merely been nerves, of course. Janet was very young for her age and she had always been a little in awe of Dominic. That was not really a good thing but it would not last once they were married and she realised how very human Dominic could be.

Helen had not forgotten Janet's tête-à-tête with Eden Varndell at Paddington or the incident of the dropped card but she had no intention of connecting Janet's recent behaviour with the man. Dominic loved Janet and wanted to marry her ... therefore Helen had helped to bring about that marriage. Janet might have known a passing attraction to another man but she would soon forget it and settle down to life with Dominic without a regret. It had obviously been a futile attraction, in any case, for she had never seen the man again to Helen's knowledge and his name had never been mentioned again ... proof that Eden Varndell could not have been interested in Janet even if she would have liked to meet him again.

Dominic's happiness was all that mattered—and Helen concentrated on the memory of Janet's devotion to him in the past and conveniently dismissed Eden Varndell from her thoughts.

It was strange that a feeling of uneasiness should persist. It was obvious that Dominic was in love with Janet so why should she be annoyed with herself for having taken Janet to task so fiercely? And was it really dismay that had filled her when Janet told her that the wedding date was decided? If so, why? She was convinced that the marriage would be the best thing for them both—or was she?

She was beginning to regret her interference. No doubt matters would have resolved themselves without her assistance. Supposing Janet really didn't care for Dominic any more ... supposing it would be a mistake for her to marry him ... supposing the marriage brought him unhappiness rather than the happiness she wanted for him? What if she had been too quick to believe that Dominic really loved and wanted to marry Janet? Perhaps he had changed his mind ... perhaps he had been the one to postpone the wedding ... perhaps he had been swept into an engagement by the impulsive Janet and sought a way out?

She stubbed her cigarette with a violent gesture. She was just going round in circles! Forget about the pair of them and concentrate on her own affairs!

Adrian's hands strayed from the keys and he turned slowly to smile at her. 'All right?'

She nodded. 'Fine.'

'You haven't touched your coffee,' he reproached.

She smiled at him. 'No ... I was listening and forgot all about it. You really do play well,

Adrian.'

He flexed his long, sensitive fingers. 'Only to an appreciative audience.'

Helen suppressed a flicker of amusement. If only he knew that she had barely heard a note of the music! It was really too bad of her to allow her thoughts to wander. He did not often agree to her request for some music and he would be most hurt if he knew that it had left her unmoved.

She held out her hand to him and he rose and went to sit by her side, slipping an arm about her slim shoulders.

'Have you finished the play?'

He scowled. 'No ... I shall have to re-write the last act.'

'Again?'

'Yes, damn it! I seem to have lost my touch.'

She laughed. 'I doubt it.'

'My mind isn't on it these days. And I never seem to have the time to ...' He broke off and Helen thought that a trace of apprehension touched his eyes.

'I thought you'd been working on it almost twenty-four hours a day,' she said with faint tartness.

'That's what it needs,' he said quickly. 'But it just isn't possible. There are so many other things to do—producers to see, my agent to talk to, people I must meet.'

Her eyes narrowed. He was a little too glib.

'Shall we call it a day, Adrian?' she asked

lightly, with seeming indifference.

He glanced at his watch. 'So early? Are you tired, my sweet?'

She sighed. 'Don't misunderstand me deliberately, Adrian.'

He rose abruptly. 'Very well. I know what you mean, of course. Do you want to end it?'

'I don't know.' She was suddenly miserable. It seemed such a pity that the bright flame should have died down to such a feeble flicker. Something had gone wrong—and she did not know when or where or why. Their love should have been great and all-embracing but the reality had never attained the heights that the beginning had promised. Had it never been love? Had she been so eager, so hungry, to love and be loved that she had seized at the first hint of the *grande passion* that came her way? Had she innocently imbued Adrian with all the qualities that she most admired and respected in a man—and then known dismay and disappointment because he did not live up to her image of him. She had warmed herself at a fierce, blazing fire and later found herself huddling close to a handful of dying embers. It would not do, of course. She had her pride and she would not cling any longer to a man who did not really want her. She had known it for weeks but refused to accept the truth. 'What went wrong?' she asked quietly, sadly.

He turned to her swiftly with compassion in his eyes. 'I wish I knew!'

'It was so perfect in the beginning.'

'Too good to last, perhaps. I'm sorry, Helen—the last thing I wanted was to hurt you. But we can't go on ... it's useless.'

'You really don't care any more ... not even a little?'

'I don't think I ever really loved you,' he said frankly. 'If I did it just died on me without warning. Love is a very capricious flame, my dear.'

She flinched at his honesty even though she welcomed it. It was like him to be blunt even at the expense of her feelings. She could only wish that he had been as honest when he first realised that he could never marry her. She had suspected a change in his feelings for weeks and clung fiercely to the hope that she was wrong— she could have been spared the weeks of uncertainty and apprehension.

'I suppose one day you'll find the woman you're seeking,' she said wearily. 'I'm just sorry it couldn't be me.'

But was she really so sorry, she wondered, as she walked briskly across the bridge to the hospital. She had refused his offer to drive her back to the Home and assured him that she would enjoy the walk. They had parted on amicable terms and Helen did not doubt his assurance that they would see each other from time to time. But she did not think that she really wanted to see Adrian again. He belonged to a part of her life that was ended. It was futile

146

to cling to the past.

She did not regret the past months. There had been much happiness in their affair ... if she could turn back the clock she would not alter anything. He had been very dear to her even if she had never been loved as she had believed.

Calmly and without the slightest pang of heartache, she confessed to herself that Adrian had been introduced into her life at a time when she particularly felt the need to love and be loved ... although she might not have realised it then. She had been more hurt than she had admitted to herself by Dominic's cold-blooded proposal. There had even been an element of defiance in her affair with Adrian ... as though she hoped to prove to Dominic that another man could love her even though he might not.

But where were her treacherous thoughts leading! It was not possible that she really wanted Dominic's love! He had never been anything more than a good friend and his proposal had merely irritated and piqued her—but why had it not amused her, why had it mattered so much? With any other man she would have laughed, dismissed him and his proposal with easy indifference and promptly forgotten all about it. But she had never forgotten Dominic's cold, unemotional proposal of marriage—and the anger he had stirred to life had never really died down.

He had been a part of her life for so many years. She had always been fond of him even while she took him for granted. If she loved him why had she not realised it before? No, this strange, haunting sadness of heart and mind could have nothing to do with Dominic! It was born of disappointment that she was not, after all, going to marry Adrian. Not because she had ever really loved him but because she had believed that each had met the one person in the world who really mattered. It was the shattering of a lovely dream that filled her with sadness.

But try though she might to keep her thoughts on Adrian, they insisted on straying to Dominic Hammond ... and he seemed so clearly etched on her mind's eye that he might have been walking by her side. Dominic ... the man she had always liked and admired despite certain traits in his character that she had deplored. Dominic ... handsome, arrogant, cold—but a man who would come to life if he was warmed by the flame of love. The capricious flame, Adrian had called it—a very apt description for an emotion that could tease and torment the heart and yet never outstay its welcome. It was an elusive flame, too—for it could live in one's heart without betraying any sign of its presence—or it could stubbornly refuse to burn brightly however much one tried to fan the flame to fiercer life.

She had tried so hard to love Adrian—tried

too hard, probably. And all the time that bright, capricious flame had only needed the fuel of a different man's image to consume her heart entirely.

Her steps slackened and she paused to stand by the stone balustrade and gaze at the dark mass of buildings that was St. Cecilia's Hospital. She thought back through the months of her training. What strange impulse had really brought her to St. Cecilia's as a student nurse? Because she had known it would annoy Dominic who, at that time, had believed that her rightful place was in his house as his wife? Because she wanted to prove that she was not just a social butterfly but a woman of intelligence and integrity, a woman worthy of his love and not just his desire for a suitable marriage? Because she had known that she would have glimpses of a different Dominic . . . the responsible, brilliant surgeon rather than the coolly courteous, mildly affectionate, always rather remote man she had known as a family friend and the occasional escort on social occasions?

Now, with the knowledge that she did indeed love Dominic Hammond, she searched her heart thoroughly and knew that he had always been the man, the only man, to fan a flame of love to bright, blazing, lasting heights.

But the knowledge had come too late. Dominic had never learned to love her—as perhaps she had always hoped deep in her heart. He had stepped down from that icy tower—but only because another woman had called to him. He was warmer, more human, less arrogant—but only because he had come to love Janet who was sweet and merry and affectionate and wholly lovable.

How could she blame Dominic? Or Janet, for that matter? She should be glad that they were both to have the happiness they deserved.

She had lost ... but the game would never have been hers, in any case. She might have married Dominic and never gone to St. Cecilia's as a nurse ... but Janet would still have trained and Dominic would have met her and fallen in love with her as he had done. The fact of his marriage to her would not have altered anything. Love came without invitation and never at anyone's bidding. She might have married Dominic and realised afterwards that she loved him—but her love would not have earned his love in return and he would have been equally heartwhole when he met Janet. These things were written in the stars—and mere mortals could not thrust aside the hand of destiny.

She could not regret her refusal to marry Dominic over a year ago ... even though she knew now that she loved him. She could not have borne to be his wife, to love him and to know that he did not care for her, that he wanted another woman and irked against the bonds of his marriage. Things had worked out well for Dominic—and she should not grudge him his happiness. Indeed, she had gone out of her way to ensure that happiness ... although she doubted that she would have been so magnanimous had she realised at the time that she wanted Dominic for herself!

It was going to be difficult to face the future with equanimity. She was already committed to the role of bridesmaid at the wedding. As a close friend of both Janet and Dominic she would be a welcome guest in their home and she could not hurt them by refusing their invitations. She would continue with her training, of course ... she had learned to love nursing and to enjoy it and it offered an escape from personal thoughts and emotions.

It could gain her nothing to betray her love for Dominic. He would be embarrassed and uncomfortable ... Janet would be hurt and unhappy and full of compassion. For the time being, it might be easier to allow them to believe that she was still engaged to Adrian ... and she looked down at the ring that still adorned her finger. Adrian had refused to take it back ... even suggested that she might like to wear it as a dress ring occasionally. She had been fully determined to toss it into the Thames as she crossed the bridge—but now she was glad that she had temporarily forgotten its existence. While she continued to wear Adrian's ring, no one would suspect that the engagement was ended and that she was not going to marry him, after all. She had not seen very much of him lately, owing to his excuses that he had to work on his play or that business demanded his attention ... she could make a point of going out one or two evenings a week, to see friends, to visit her home and parents. She had always been reticent about her personal affairs and Janet and Sally would not think it odd that she did not talk about Adrian. In any case, the main subject of the conversation for the next few weeks would be Janet's wedding and Janet's future. It would be painful to have to listen, to have to join in the discussions—but there was nothing else she could do without arousing suspicion.

Above all, she must not do or say anything to mar Janet's happiness ... even though she might not seem as happy as one would expect of a girl about to be married, it had always been obvious to her friends that she adored Dominic and her recent oddness of manner could only be attributed to nervousness. If the man she had met on the train, coming back to the hospital after her holiday, had really stirred an attraction to life, Janet would not have agreed to marry Dominic in the first place. She had far too much integrity.

So there was no point in hoping that Janet might even yet change her mind ... and while Dominic's happiness was at stake she must not be allowed to even think of changing her mind and hurting him desperately!

She walked on as Big Ben struck the hour. She would be late but she did not really care. Home Sister would scold, as usual—but Helen felt that she had other things on her mind much more important than a trivial scold because of a few minutes' lateness...

Dominic was just drawing away from the Home but he braked swiftly as he recognised Helen as she walked towards him. She glanced at the car and then paused involuntarily.

He opened the door and stepped out, calling her name. Slowly she walked along the pavement to him. He looked down at her, his eyes cold with anger ... but Helen did not realise the implication of his expression.

'Hallo, Dominic. I can't stay ... I'm late now. Have you just brought Janet home?' They had not met since Janet had informed her friends that the wedding date was fixed—and because of her recent thoughts about him and the realisation of her love for him, she was grateful to her lateness which forbade her to pause for more than a moment.

'Yes ... we've been discussing wedding arrangements,' he said coldly.

She nodded. 'I gather it's going to be quite a big affair.'

'All women want white weddings, don't they? For myself, I'd be content with a registrar and a handful of close friends.'

'I'm glad you've finally fixed a date, Dominic.' She forced a bright smile. 'There

153

really wasn't much point in waiting any longer for your happiness. You seem to have waited so long already.'

'Yes ... Janet told me that you'd persuaded her to fix a date.' Suddenly his anger spilled over. 'You seem to have been very busy in my affairs—like all women, you can't wait to see the noose about a man's neck ... provided you're not the bride, in this case!'

She stared at him, astonished. 'What on earth do you mean?'

He already regretted his words. He had said too much ... but all evening he had been simmering with anger, ever since Janet had shyly confessed that she had been a little unsure of her feelings, a little nervous, and that Helen had made her realise how foolish she was being and how hurt he must have been by her seeming reluctance to set the day for their wedding. He could cheerfully have throttled Helen in that moment!

He forced laughter into his voice. 'I know you're engrossed in thoughts of marriage yourself and therefore can't wait to see all your friends in the same happy state—but no man likes to think that his bride has been talked into setting the date by her friends, you know.'

'It isn't like that at all!' she hastened to assure him. 'Janet was afraid that you might not really want to marry her ... I know that's why she hasn't been very happy lately!'

He was taken aback. He had tried so hard to

conceal his real feelings ... and Janet had never given any sign that she suspected any lack in his ardour or wish to marry her.

'Are you sure?'

'Quite sure,' she said firmly.

'But Janet never talked to me about it. ...'

'Of course not! She was terrified that she might be right ... that you'd changed your mind. She didn't want to force the issue. Naturally, I assured her that you really do love her—and that you were hurt because she wouldn't decide on a date. It's true, isn't it?'

He sighed. It was much too late to deny her conception of the circumstances ... much too late to take her in his arms and assure her that she was the only woman he loved and that he could not possibly go through with his proposed marriage to Janet, sweet though she was.

'I realise that you were only concerned with my happiness, Helen ... thank you. But if Janet had any doubts about her feelings ...'

'She doubted *your* feelings!' she told him emphatically. Whether or not it was the truth did not seem to matter—she knew that the only important thing was that Dominic should have for his wife the woman he loved. If the thought crossed her mind that Janet had doubted her own feelings rather than his she suppressed it firmly. Janet did not really know what she wanted or she would never allow herself to think of another man even for a moment. Once she was married to Dominic she would have ample opportunity to appreciate the good qualities of the man who was her husband and she would cease to think of Eden Varndell ... and Helen firmly stifled the vague uneasiness that seemed to insist that Janet had really been interested in the writer and that her recent unhappiness stemmed from his indifference and the fact that she was engaged to a man she did not really love.

She did not give Dominic time to argue the matter further. With a smile and a swift goodnight, she left him to face an irate Home Sister ...

CHAPTER TWELVE

Janet approached the Nurses Home and glanced idly at a tall young man who seemed to be waiting for someone by the gates. He walked up and down uncertainly, glanced frequently at his watch and then at the raw brick building, turned swiftly at the sound of footsteps and scanned the faces of those who approached.

He glanced at Janet, took a step towards her and then hesitated. She paused, an enquiry in her eyes and tentative smile.

'Can I help you?'

'Perhaps you can,' he said eagerly. 'Do you

know a Nurse Calvert?'

'Sally Calvert ... yes, very well. We share a room,' she told him easily.

'Oh? Then you'll know if she's on or off duty now, won't you? I'm a ... friend of Sally's. We come from the same town.'

'She should be off duty, I think. I'll find out for you, if you'll wait a few minutes. Does she know you're in London?'

'Well ... I told her I might be around this way but we didn't fix a definite date.'

Janet smiled at him warmly. He seemed rather nervous and she wondered if he was uncertain of his reception. It was quite time that Sally had a boyfriend ... she was so shy, so reserved. She was on friendly terms with lots of the students and housemen, as were most of the nurses, but she did not seem to be interested in anyone in particular. Perhaps she would feel more at ease with a man from her own part of the world. And maybe this rather good-looking man had been one of her dates before she came to St. Cecilia's and now wanted to pick up old threads.

'She'll be pleased to see you, I expect,' she assured him. 'But it's a bit risky to turn up without warning, if you don't mind me telling you so. It's always safer to telephone in advance ... nurses don't have a great deal of free time, you know.'

'Yes ... I will in future. Do you think ... you said you'd find out for me if Sally's around or on duty,' he reminded her, a little curtly.

'Yes, of course.' She was slightly taken aback by the chilliness of his tone. Obviously her advice had been unwelcome although her only thought had been to save him a possible disappointment in the future.

She left him and passed through the gates and entered the Home. She checked the board and confirmed her belief that Sally was off duty. She hurried up the wide staircase to their room on the sixth floor, scarcely noticing the stairs now although they had been a constant cause for grumbling in the early days of their training.

Sally was looking through her clothes in the wardrobe, her uniform dress and its appendages lying on her bed.

'I'm glad you're in,' Janet said without preliminary. 'You're not going out, are you? On a date, I mean?'

Sally looked at her in surprise. 'Nowhere very special ... why?'

'There's someone to see you,' she announced with a twinkle in her eyes. 'A very dashing young man waiting by the gates in the hope of catching you on your way in or out.'

Sally was puzzled. 'A young man—who? One of the students?'

'I shouldn't think so. He said that he came from Hurley and was an old friend.'

She was suddenly very pale and then colour rushed hotly to her face. 'Did he ... give you his name?' she asked, turning back to the wardrobe to hide her flaming face.

'I didn't think to ask,' she admitted ruefully. 'And he didn't mention it. But I expect you'd recognise a description ... fairly tall, fair hair, brown eyes, good looking, well-dressed, pleasant speaking voice...'

'Yes. I know who is it,' Sally said in muffled tones. She had not needed a description to guess that it was Roger who was hanging about outside the Home. She wondered why he had not telephoned. Perhaps he had come on a mere impulse at the last minute. Certainly he had suggested that they should meet when he came to London but she had not really believed that he meant it—and no doubt he hadn't meant it until he found himself in London, thought of her in passing and decided to look her up.

Did she really want to see him? Yes, of course she wanted to ... but she was afraid. She had already been hurt so much by Roger—she was still vulnerable where he was concerned and she must not forget that he was a married man and that he couldn't really mean anything by wanting to see her. He was probably bored or had an hour to spare before keeping an appointment somewhere ... she closed her mind to the memory of the hunger in his eyes and the faint bitterness in his voice at their last meeting. It was dangerous to think even for a moment that he might regret breaking their engagement to marry Mavis ... even more dangerous to meet him again when she was having so much trouble with her rebellious heart. For she was still in love with Roger ... neither time nor separation had altered the way she felt about him. That brief, chance meeting a few weeks before had only impressed upon her the impossibility of ceasing to love him, of forgetting him completely in the work she had chosen to do at St. Cecilia's.

'An old flame? He looked awfully nice.'

'Yes ... he is nice.' Abruptly she turned to look at Janet and the words came tumbling out impulsively: 'It's Roger ... and I don't know what to do. I want to see him—but I know he shouldn't have come ... and I wish I knew why he has!'

'Roger ... you mean your ex-fiancé, the man you were going to marry?'

Sally nodded miserably. 'I ran into him when I was home ... on my way back here, actually. He gave me a lift to the station and ... oh, Janet, I've been feeling so wretched ever since!' She sat down on her bed and buried her face in her hands.

Janet was aghast. She had been so absorbed in her own affairs that she had not even noticed that Sally wasn't happy ... and all the time she had evidently been eating her heart out for a man who had let her down and married her best friend. Dismayed, touched by Sally's tears, she sat down by her side and put an arm about the thin shoulders.

'I thought you'd got over it long ago,' she said awkwardly.

'So did I!' she wailed through her tears. 'But I haven't ... and I can't see him, Jan, I can't!'

'Well, you don't have to, ducky,' she said firmly. 'I'll go down and tell him you're on duty ... no wonder he didn't try to phone you first. He must have known you wouldn't see him so he's been hanging about in the hope of catching you. He hasn't any right to pester you when he's married—and I've a good mind to tell him so!'

'No!' Sally clutched at her apron. 'I'll tell him, Janet. I shall have to go down ... he may have been waiting there for ages. I came off duty early with toothache otherwise I would probably have seen him. I shall have to see him—but I wish he hadn't come!' She brushed her hand across her eyes and rose to her feet. She went to the wash-basin and splashed her face with cold water and then ran a comb through her hair. Hastily she slipped into the first dress that came to her hand. Janet watched her, frowning. She did not think that Sally was being very wise—but it was entirely her affair.

After all, would she be as wise if it was Eden who had gone out of his way to find her—even if she was already married to Dominic? She knew that, loving him as she did, she would risk anything to see him if only for a few minutes—even the risk of renewed heartache

161

and longing.

Sally moved to the door. Her heart was thudding painfully and her knees were like water but she was outwardly composed.

'Don't worry, Jan ... I'll send him away with a flea in his ear and I doubt if he'll bother to get in touch with me again,' she said with much more determination than she really felt.

It was easy to say such a thing to her friend— but as she went nervously down the stairs, almost stumbling in her haste, she knew that it would take far more courage than she possessed to tell Roger that he must go away and not try to see her again.

He started towards her as she hurried towards the gates. 'Sally!'

'Hallo, Roger,' she said weakly, resolution failing as she met those warm brown eyes and knew again the joyful happiness in his affectionate smile.

'My usual luck is with me,' he said boyishly. 'If I'd known you were in I'd have gone up to the house and asked for you.'

'I'm glad you didn't. What are you doing here, anyway?'

'Looking for you,' he said lightly. 'How about lunch?'

'I'm supposed to report to the dentist at two o'clock,' she demurred.

'Well, that leaves you plenty of time,' he told her and tucked her hand in his arm in a possessive gesture. 'You won't need a coat on a day like this. Come on ... the Atom Bomb is just round the corner.'

She was swept along by his easy command of the situation and within a few moments she found herself by his side in the small sports car.

'I ... I didn't expect to see you,' she faltered.

He turned to smile at her. 'I told you I'd be in London within a few weeks ... and you did say that you'd like to have lunch with me.'

'Yes, I know ... but ...'

'No buts! You never used to be so argumentative, Sally—I don't think you should have taken up nursing.'

'It was never my intention,' she reminded him tartly.

He coloured slightly. 'Don't be difficult, darling,' he chided in the tone that had always managed to put her in the wrong. 'I made a mistake ... I'm perfectly willing to admit that. But we all make mistakes. You're not going to hold it over my head for the rest of my life, are you?'

She caught her breath. 'I doubt if there'll be any opportunities,' she said slowly, with difficulty.

He reached for her hand and pressed it warmly, meaningfully, 'There will be, darling.'

She wrenched her hand away. 'I don't know what you mean, Roger.'

He cast her a reproachful glance. 'Don't be unkind, Sally. What's wrong ... don't you love me these days?'

She stiffened. 'Should I? Do you think that

your behaviour earned my undying love? You seem to forget that you dropped me like a hot brick just because you were smitten with Mavis!'

'Smitten is the word,' he agreed with a faint sigh. 'I've made a thorough mess of everything. I was sure you still cared for me, Sally—if I'd known that you'd changed your mind about me I wouldn't have walked out on Mavis.' There was a note of sulkiness in his tone.

'Walked out on Mavis!' Sally was horrified. 'Oh, no! You can't mean it ... you can't mean that you've left her—oh, Roger ... and she's going to have a baby!'

He shrugged. 'It's never worked, Sally—and I don't see what difference the baby makes. It wasn't my idea in the first place—and to tell the truth, I'm sick to death of the blasted baby. Mavis never talks about anything else! I've had a noose round my neck for nearly a year and every day it's been tightened a little more—you just don't know what it's like, Sally. I'm not taking any more—and that's final! I thought perhaps we could make a fresh start, darling— and later on, when I get a divorce, we can get married.'

Sally stared at him, horrified. She had never thought it possible that Roger could be a stranger—but certainly she did not know this man who talked so airily and glibly of fresh starts and divorce in the same breath as he sneered at his wife and spoke of his own expected child with loathing in his voice.

'No!' She spoke firmly, decisively.

Roger pulled into the kerb and turned off the ignition. 'What do you mean ... no? I've thrown over everything for you ... Mavis, my chances of having my own garage, my future...'

'Not at my request or suggestion,' she reminded him tartly.

'But I did it for you ...!'

'No, you didn't, Roger. You did it for yourself! You've always been as selfish as a man can be—and this is just another example of your selfishness. If your marriage is such a wash-out then I think you're to blame—not Mavis. Just because you're fed up with being married and feeling jealous and neglected because Mavis is naturally excited and pleased about having a baby, you've simply washed your hands of everything—just like you washed your hands of me when you thought you'd get a better bargain in Mavis. Well, don't drag me into your sordid little affairs! It was none of my doing that you left your wife—and I won't let you neatly slip the blame on to my shoulders. You've always been too quick with that trick, Roger. The trouble with you is that you've never really grown up! You want everything to go your way ... and when it doesn't you won't play, just like a silly, sulky little boy! I think you're despicable!'

It was his turn to stare. No one had ever

thrown so many hard truths into his face in his life. Petted and indulged by loving parents, charming and attractive enough to win friends easily and to persuade them to fall in with his wishes and plans, everything going to his advantage in the past, he simply could not believe that Sally had not fallen into his arms with a cry of happiness and eagerly discussed his plans for their future with him. He did not know this Sally ... this bright-eyed, sharp-tongued, fiery little termagant whose tone left him in no doubt as to her opinion of him.

'Well, if that's what you think of me, there's nothing more to say, is there?' he asked quietly, almost stunned into meekness.

'Nothing at all ... except goodbye! I don't want to see or hear from you again, Roger Gale—and the only news I want of you is that you've gone back to Mavis and faced your responsibilities like a grown man! Then perhaps I'll manage to feel a little respect for you—at the moment, I can only wonder how on earth I ever thought that I loved you! Thank heavens that you did prefer Mavis ... I imagine you must be the world's worst husband!'

With that parting shot, she wrenched open the car door, scrambled out and stalked away from him, her eyes blazing with fury, her whole body stiff with indignation and contempt.

What a little fool she had been ... to go down to meet him trembling and nervous, to greet him with eager affection, to melt at one glance

166

from those brown eyes, to expand under the warmth of his treacherous smile, to allow him to sweep her off to his car as though she had no mind of her own. Oh, no wonder he had it all cut and dried! She had behaved like a lovesick fool that day when he had taken her to the station ... and Roger, already tired of Mavis and her enthusiasm for her coming child, had probably considered that he would be better off with a girl who thought he was wonderful and showed it than with Mavis who had always been a little temperamental and demanding and would not hesitate to do battle royal with him if he annoyed her. And Sally had never dared to argue with him, to go against his wishes or suggestions, had fallen in gladly with all his plans, had adored him openly and bolstered his ego and almost smothered him with affection. Oh, she had been too sweet, too clinging, too loyal, too willing—no wonder he had found Mavis attractive in comparison! Obviously they had crossed swords too often to please Roger who liked to be kingpin in his little world—so he had decided that his marriage was a mistake and assumed with all his natural, stupendous conceit that Sally would welcome him with open arms!

Well, he had been wrong. Her eyes had finally been opened to the weakness and viciousness of his character—and she had realised that she had idolised a Roger Gale who did not exist, a dream, a god on a pedestal.

The real man was someone she could not even like ... and it seemed incredible that she could like next door to Roger all those years, know him intimately, be engaged to him and yet find him to be a complete stranger. She had been blinded by the veil of fantasy that she had called love—but the veil had been abruptly torn from her eyes and she would never again be troubled by heartache or longing for the man she had once planned to marry ...

As she reached the Home, a faint smile curved her lips. Well, she had done what she had told Janet she would do—sent him away with a flea in his ear and told him never to seek her out again. But although she had spoken firmly enough to Janet, she had not really believed that she could have the courage or the strength of mind to carry out her threat. She had been so sure that he would break down her every defence ... so sure that she would weakly agree to a clandestine affair if that was what he wanted as long as she could still see him and bask in his love.

Love! Roger Gale had never loved anyone but himself—and probably never would. He would never know the joy or the agony of being in love ... and Sally could almost feel sorry for him.

She would never again mistake her own feelings, she knew. The next time she loved a man—if there was a next time—she would not endow him with impossible virtues, set him on a pedestal, convince herself that he could do and say no wrong. The next time she loved she would bring a mature heart and mind to the business of loving—and if destiny was on her side it would not be a one-sided affair next time! She would know what it meant to be loved by a man she could like and respect and admire as well as love—and she would know all the security and peace of mind and quiet affinity of true love truly shared by a man and a woman...

'You were a long time,' Janet said as she went into their room.

'Longer than I meant to be,' she agreed.

'I thought he'd talked you into having lunch with him.'

She smiled and her voice was light and gay as she returned easily: 'The days are past when Roger Gale can talk me into anything, Janet.'

'You sound awfully pleased with yourself,' Janet said curiously. 'What's happened?'

'I've just been cured of a lingering disease,' she retorted blithely. 'And you can't imagine how good it feels. I should have known that being in love wouldn't make anyone as miserable as I've been these last few weeks— even if it seems to be pretty hopeless at least one can't help the song in one's heart, I should think.'

Janet bent her head swiftly over the blouse she was mending. She did not want to disillusion Sally but she thought unhappily

169

that she could do with a few notes of a song to cheer her aching, lonely heart. Perhaps the ache would grow less as time passed ... at the moment she wanted nothing more than Eden's presence, his arms about her, the soft, sweet touch of his lips, the murmur of his voice—and if that miracle ever came about then there would indeed be a song in her heart ... a glad paeon of thanksgiving to a kindly destiny...

CHAPTER THIRTEEN

'Another day nearer.'

Janet forced a bleak smile and carried on down the corridor. So many people went out of their way to remind her of the approaching wedding—as if she needed to be reminded!

Every dawn brought her wedding day nearer—and every night Janet settled for sleep praying that a miracle would happen.

She was not sleeping well and the anxiety and unhappiness of her dilemma had driven the natural, healthy colour from her cheeks. But when her friends commented on her appearance, she brushed aside their concern with a light reference to last-minute nerves or to the many things on her mind connected with the wedding.

Dominic did not seem to notice her pallor—or perhaps he merely forbore to

170

mention it. It seemed incredible that he could not be aware of her lack of enthusiasm for wedding plans, her reluctance to be embraced or kissed—but no doubt he also had things on his mind and thought there was time enough in the future for love-making.

She was dreading the future as his wife. Kind though he was, gentle and understanding and sympathetic, always considerate, he was rapidly taking on the proportions of an ogre.

At night, groping for elusive sleep, her feverish mind would paint pictures of life with a demanding, difficult, impatient husband who had married a young girl in order to mould her to his liking. These fantasies were immediately dismissed when she saw him again ... but they insisted on tormenting her again when night fell and she went to her bed.

If only it could be Eden who would be waiting for her at the altar, waiting to take her hand and to exchange vows with her, waiting to share his life, his dreams, his hopes and disappointments, with her. If only it could be Eden who loved her as Dominic loved her ... but it was not Eden for he had forgotten her completely or surely he would have been in touch with her some way. No man who felt any interest in a girl would completely ignore her existence—or leave it to her whim to see her again! He had been kind and friendly when she went to his house ... but perhaps in reality he had been annoyed and resentful of her obvious interest.

There was nothing she could do ... she would have to marry Dominic, go through with the big, impressive ceremony that she dreaded.

And then Janet halted as a sudden, blinding thought flashed into her mind. What a crass fool she was! Of course she didn't *have* to marry Dominic ... no power on earth could impel her to go through with it even at this late date!

Why had she allowed herself to be swept along like a piece of flotsam on a heavy tide? Did she have no mind of her own? Was she really so weak, so spineless, so fearful of the gossip she would incur by breaking her engagement when there was less than a week to the wedding?

Had she really intended to go through with it—to marry a man she did not love on the weak plea that she could not destroy his happiness? What happiness could she guarantee him in the future ... a wife who did not love him and who could not forget that she *did* love another man? Even though he loved her, Dominic would not want an unwilling bride, surely ... he was too proud, too integral, too kind! He would understand and forgive ... loving her as he did, he would be concerned for her happiness perhaps even more than his own.

It would be neither just nor sensible to marry Dominic, *knowing* that she was merely fond of him and could never love him.

How utterly selfish she had been during these past weeks! How unkind and thoughtless! Dominic was not a fool—he must have sensed her withdrawal, her indifference, her reluctance to marry him. But because he loved her so much he had been patient and understanding, assuring himself that all would be well once she was his wife—cold comfort indeed for the way she had treated him! She had behaved very shabbily—and she felt thoroughly ashamed now.

It would have been so much kinder, so much more honest, to have told him the truth when she first met Eden Varndell and knew that he would always mean more to her than Dominic. She should never have drifted into their engagement merely because her mind had been full of Eden and she had agreed to marry Dominic, not even fully aware of what he had been asking her.

Certainly she shouldn't have continued with this farce for several weeks ... and she was hot with shame as she admitted for the first time that she had allowed Dominic to believe that she would marry him only because she dreaded to be left without either him or Eden ... because she knew that she would never see Eden again and her love seemed so hopeless that she had convinced herself that it didn't matter very much if she did marry a man who loved her anyway. How could she have been so absorbed with her own feelings as to disregard Dominic's right to a wife who loved him, to the happiness that could only come of marriage based on mutual, sincere and lasting love?

Thank heavens she had come to her senses before it was too late! Certainly it would be neither easy nor pleasant to call off the wedding so late in the day—but she had only herself to blame.

She was in love with a man who had forgotten her existence—so what? It must happen to hundreds of others—but surely no one else was quite so silly as to rush into marriage with the first man at hand just because she couldn't have the man she did want!

She would always love Eden. There could never be anyone else to replace him in her heart. She could never again contemplate marriage with someone other than Eden—and as that was evidently out of the question it was quite time she faced the fact that she would never marry. She had her career ... and that had been important to her until these last few weeks. It could be so again. Nursing was definitely a preferable and more worthwhile use for her life than spending it with a man she did not love—and nurses would always be in demand!

Now that she had realised what she must do she determined not to postpone the unpleasant task of telling Dominic that she could not marry him. She would go round to his house that very evening. It would mean cutting a lecture but she would have all the time in the world to devote to her training in the future ... at the moment it was imperative that she shouldn't continue to deceive the man who had done nothing to merit the hurt and disappointment that she had to inflict on him ...

Dominic tried to concentrate on the evening papers but his rebellious thoughts would keep reverting to Janet and the wedding that loomed ever nearer.

He was completely baffled. He just did not understand Janet at all—and yet he had believed her to be so open, so easy to read, so straightforward.

There had been nothing straightforward or open in her behaviour of the last few weeks. He could not help suspecting that she did not want to marry him, that she had changed her mind or that she no longer cared for him. Not only did she keep him at arms' length as much as possible but she seemed averse to being alone with him and strove desperately to guide the conversation into other channels whenever the wedding or their future together was mentioned.

But if Janet had undergone a change of heart—why didn't she tell him and release him from an engagement he had never wanted in his heart? What were her motives in going through with the wedding?

If only he knew her real feelings! Suspicion was not enough. How could he demand to know if she really wanted to marry him? It was only too possible that her odd manner could be explained away ... Helen had claimed that Janet doubted his feelings ... she had also told him that Janet was suffering from nervousness as the wedding approached. All very feasible. Women did suffer from an attack of nerves just before marriage in many cases. It was possible that Janet had sensed his lack of ardour, his hungry need of another woman, and was too afraid of him to tackle him—or too afraid that her fears might be confirmed and she would lose him.

He did not want to marry Janet ... and he admitted that he had fostered his suspicions hopefully. He also admitted that he had been trying to persuade her to end their engagement in subtle ways ... by impressing on her that once he had a hostess for his table he intended to entertain on a lavish scale, by insisting on a large, slightly vulgar and ornate wedding that would try the nerves of an Amazon, by sketching grim pictures of what her life would be as a busy surgeon's wife, by talking airily of his indifference to children and his hope that Janet would not insist on adding to the household ...

He knew that she was a little shy and awed by grandeur. He knew that she would feel like a fish out of water in the midst of a motley collection of his wealthy, extravagant, sophisticated friends. He knew that she shrank from the thought of playing the part of hostess to a crowd of people who were complete strangers and lived in a different world to the one she had always known.

He knew that she would have preferred a quiet, simple wedding, attended only by close family and intimate friends, followed by a tour of Devon and Cornwall or a fortnight in the Lake District. She had not raised any objections to his plans for a wedding at St. Margaret's attended by over two hundred guests, a reception at the Savoy and a honeymoon in the South of France ... but he knew that her sensitive, shy nature had instinctively shrank from his suggestions.

He knew that she would be perfectly content to run a small house, to tend a small garden, to enjoy the simple things of life with a man who was not constantly in demand and had little time to enjoy his wife and his home. She did not relish the thought of living in the big expensively-furnished house that was competently run by haughty but well trained servants with whom she would have to cope. He knew that she had always been a little nervous with Travers—and he also knew that she had always been conscious of the man's disapproval.

He knew that Janet loved children and

would want her own in due course. She believed that no marriage could be happy or complete without children—and that those who were childless through no fault of of their own should offer a home and affection to a child who had no family. In his heart, Dominic agreed—but it had not been his intention to betray the fact.

Yet, despite all these things, she was still determined to marry him. Which argued that she really did love him, much more than he deserved, or that she had her own, unknown motives at which he could not even guess.

Dominic realised the wrong he would be committing by marrying Janet in the full knowledge that he did not and never could love her. But he had been so convinced that she would not go through with it that he had allowed matters to drift. And now, with less than a week to the wedding, he was beginning to appreciate that he was caught in his own trap. *He* could not back out—for if Janet had no intention of doing so he could only believe that she loved him. He would not attribute ulterior motives to a girl like Janet. So it seemed that within a week he would be a married man—and all he could do to atone for his lack of love was to ensure that their marriage brought as much happiness as possible to his wife.

He had been sincere when he asked her to marry him. He had believed that they could make a tolerable success of marriage ... he had been sure then of her love for him and that his affection for Janet was sufficient. But he had soon realised that he could not live a lie for the rest of his life. If he could not have the woman he wanted then it would be better to end his days a bachelor! But by then things had gone too far ... and now there seemed no avenue of escape...

At the sound of the doorbell, he glanced up absently from his newspaper. He was not expecting anyone this evening but perhaps a friend had decided to call in for a drink. He stifled a feeling of annoyance and forced a smile to his lips as the door opened.

He rose abruptly. 'Janet! I thought you had a lecture tonight.'

'I did ... I cut it,' she said simply.

'I suppose there isn't really much point in bothering about lectures now. You'll be finished with nursing at the end of the week.' He went to pour her the sweet sherry that she liked.

'No, I won't.'

He turned to look at her steadily. 'You won't?'

'I've withdrawn my notice ... and Matron was kind enough not to comment.'

His heart was thudding with new hope but he knew that he would have to tread warily. There could be so many explanations for the withdrawal of her notice...

'You want to carry on with your training? Well ... I suppose it's quite a good idea. It will take you some time to adjust to being married and as I'm seldom at home you'd often be pretty lonely. But it's a hasty decision, isn't it?'

She ignored his question. 'I'm sorry, Dominic ... but I'm not going to marry you. I ... can't!' Her voice broke slightly.

He placed her sherry on a low table and drew her down to sit by his side on the long couch. 'What's all this?' he asked gently. 'Butterflies, Janet?'

'No ... it's just that—I can't marry you!'

He took her hand and prised open the clenched fingers. 'You're so tense ... don't be anxious, Janet. I'm not going to rave at you for changing your mind. You really mean it, I suppose? This isn't just an attack of nerves?'

She shook her head. 'I've known all the time—I shouldn't have agreed to marry you, I shouldn't have let you give me a ring. I've behaved despicably—and you've every right to be furious.'

'You're not in love with me?'

'No ... I'm sorry, Dominic, really sorry. I ... thought I loved you ... once. But I know now that I never did. It's just ... well, you were different, more mature, more worldly. I suppose I was flattered and thrilled that you liked me—I suppose you'll never forgive me?'

'There's nothing to forgive. I understand— believe me, I understand! There's someone

180

else, Janet?'

'Oh, not really ... I mean, yes—well, no....'

He smiled down at her tenderly. 'Take your time, my dear.'

'It's all pretty hopeless!' she blurted.

He nodded. So she *was* in love with someone else—someone who did not care for her in return. He could understand and wholly sympathise ... and even appreciate why she had considered marrying him and allowed him and everyone else to believe that she would do so. It was strange that Janet should have followed the same line of thought as himself—stranger still that he had not realised weeks ago that she was in love with someone else. Now he understood her unhappiness, her distrait air, her reluctance to be alone with him and to accept his love-making, her weary indifference to the wedding plans and his warnings as to what her future life would be.

'I'm sorry ... but perhaps it isn't as hopeless as it seems at the moment,' he comforted. 'After all, you have been engaged to me for some weeks—and perhaps the man doesn't realise that you care for him.'

'I wouldn't want him to know!' she said in alarm.

'All very natural ... but sometimes love has to be helped a little, you know. Left to itself it can get tied up in the most complicated knots.' He thought ruefully that it was scarcely meet for him to give such advice when he loved

181

Helen and yet had never attempted to help his love in any way—but circumstances were the same in his case ... she was engaged to another man and he had no reason to believe that his suit would stand a chance.

'I'm sorry that I've left it so late ... and I never meant you to be hurt, Dominic. I know I've treated you abominably—and it won't be very pleasant for you to have everyone knowing that I've jilted you at the last moment.'

He smiled. 'Not quite the last moment ... you might have waited until the wedding day and then failed to arrive at the church. Don't worry about me, Janet. If anyone offers me consolation I shall throw them the hoary line that it's better to realise a mistake before marriage than after—and that's perfectly true, you know. I admire you, Janet—it takes a lot of courage to admit that you can't go through with it, after all ... and I'm grateful to you for sparing us both a great deal of misery. It would never have worked out—but perhaps we will both be luckier in the future.'

'You've taken it very well,' she said wonderingly. 'Don't you mind, Dominic?'

'Well ... let's just say that I appreciate that it would have been a mistake. Marriage is always a gamble ... it doesn't help to start off on the wrong foot without the one thing that might guarantee its success and its happiness.'

'Love, you mean?'

'Mutual love,' he amended quietly—and his smile was very warm and very sympathetic and oddly comforting...

CHAPTER FOURTEEN

Dominic sat back in his chair with a deep sigh of relief and thankfulness. Well, that was a very tricky problem that would no longer trouble him! His intuition had proved to be right ... Janet did not love him and there was no longer any need to take vows that did not come from the heart or to live a lie for the rest of his life!

There would be gossip and speculation ... but he had survived both in the past and would do so again. He hoped that the gossips would not deal too harshly with Janet ... she was not used to the exposure of her private affairs and she was a sensitive girl. She must have gone through an agony of mind during the past weeks ... he devoutly hoped that things would come right for her eventually.

Perhaps now he could turn his mind to the events of the day ... and he picked up his discarded newspaper with a lighter heart.

But it seemed that he was not destined to enjoy a quiet evening in which to relax after a heavy day in the theatre. Janet had been gone scarcely an hour when the doorbell shrilled again ... and he wondered if she had returned to assure him that she would marry him, after all.

But it was Helen who hurried into the room without ceremony... a Helen who had scarcely paused to powder her nose and apply lipstick and run a comb through her hair ... a Helen who still wore her uniform with her red cloak thrown hastily about her shoulders ... a Helen whose eyes were bright with the light of battle.

'This is an unexpected pleasure,' he drawled, rising to his feet.

'Dominic, I had to come! I knew you'd be in a terrible state! How could she treat you so ... I'll never forgive her for this! But you needn't worry, Dominic... she'll marry you if I have to drag her to the church myself. It's nothing but nerves ... she's desperately in love with you. I know Janet—and I *know*! She's just had the lecture of her life ... and I haven't finished with her...'

He interrupted the angry flow of words. 'My dear Helen, I hope you haven't been bullying Janet.' Leisurely he crossed to the decanters. Leisurely he poured drinks for them both. Leisurely he turned to smile at her with amusement in his eyes.

She stared at him in amazement. He seemed so cool, so unperturbed ... but Dominic was ever one to hide his real feelings under a cloak of lightness.

'I know how you must be feeling,' she said soberly. 'I could have throttled Janet when she told me about it! I didn't know she could be so cruel! But she doesn't mean it, Dominic ... believe me, she wants to marry you and tomorrow morning she'll be crying her eyes out because she called off the wedding...'

'I'll throttle you if you don't stop meddling in things that don't concern you,' he said lightly.

'Meddling!' She was hurt and dismayed.

'What do *you* call it? I told you once before that you're too busy in my affairs,' he said grimly ... and then regretted immediately the harshness of his tone. She could not realise how ironic it was that she should be so concerned to marry him off to another woman!

'Oh!' It was an involuntary exclamation of pain. Then she tilted her chin proudly. 'It seems that I rushed here for nothing. Forgive my interference ... apparently it's bad manners to try to help one's friends.'

She turned and stalked to the door. He reached her side and caught her arm. 'But you haven't helped, Helen—I know your motives were good and I appreciate your friendly interest. But please ... Janet and I have settled matters amicably ... don't try to confuse things now!'

Completely bewildered, she scanned his handsome face. 'But ... I don't understand ... You seem quite pleased that Janet isn't going to marry you! Don't you want to marry Janet?'

'No ... and I never did,' he said ruefully.

185

'But ... you *were* engaged—you did propose!'

He gave a small shrug. 'Shall we call it a mutual misunderstanding—and leave it at that?' His smile evoked no response in the angry woman by his side.

'That's great ... when I've spent hours impressing on Janet how much you care about her and what a wonderful husband you'll make! When I've been worrying myself silly in case she called off the engagement and made you a laughing-stock at the hospital! When I've done all I could to prevent you from being hurt a second time!' She wrenched her arm from his hand. 'I do think you might have told me that you were only playing a silly game of your own!'

He closed the door firmly for a second time and stood with his back against the panels so that, other than struggling with him, she could not leave the room.

'Your concern for my peace of mind has puzzled me a great deal,' he said quietly. 'Why were you so eager to push Janet into marrying me? Why should you care if our affair became the talk of the hospital? What does it matter to you whether or not I get hurt?'

'Oh, you fool!' she snapped, beside herself with fury. 'Because I love you—so much it hurts! Because I wanted you to be happy—and if Janet was the woman you wanted then I meant to see that you had what you wanted!

186

Does that satisfy you?'

He was pale with the shock of her words. He stared at her for a long moment in silence. It was incredible that Helen should love him, should have loved him while he was planning to marry another woman—and should have kept her secret so well.

'But—you're engaged to Hart,' he said blankly.

She tore the ring from her finger and threw it to the floor. 'Was! Was engaged! Past tense, Dominic! It was broken days ago.'

'Yet you still wear his ring,' he pointed out.

'Because I'm a coward! Because I couldn't face questions and gossip and rumours! Because I was afraid that Janet and Sally might guess why I finished with Adrian!'

'I see.' He moved away from the door, went to stand by the fireplace with his hand on the mantel, at a complete loss for the first time in his life. She had thrown her love at him in anger ... she was still furious with him. How could he take her in his arms and tell her that he loved her, had always loved her? She would never believe that he was sincere ... men in love did not engage themselves to other women ... at the risk of pain and humiliation they went after the one woman they wanted ... he had given up too easily, had convinced himself too readily that Helen did not give him a second thought—a fine, ardent, courageous lover to offer any woman!

'I seem to have made a fool of myself,' she said unsteadily, her anger vanquished by the realisation of all that she had said in temper.

'That makes two of us, then,' he retorted crisply. He swung round to look at her with a plea in his eyes. 'I wish I'd known the truth, Helen ... was it so impossible to tell me how you felt? Did you have to punish me by pretending to care for Hart?'

'Punish you?'

'Isn't that what you were doing? Taking a sweet revenge for the insult I offered? Trying to impress on me that not every man wanted to marry you because you were "suitable"? Do you know how often I've cursed that damned proposal I made? Do you realise how much I've regretted talking to you so airily about marriage and the fantasy of love? Fantasy ... my God! If this hell is fantasy then let me return to reality with all speed!'

She moved slowly into the middle of the room. 'We seem to have made a fine tangle between us, Dominic.'

He laughed grimly. 'How right you are!'

'It isn't too late to unravel it,' she said gently—and held out her hands to him in a gesture that was almost supplication.

He moved swiftly to take her hands, to clasp them firmly, to search the lovely face and the violet eyes that sought his own so hungrily— and found what they sought. A tiny sigh of thankfulness and relief hovered on her lips ...

and then he claimed the lips and the arms he had longed to know for so many weary, self-reproaching months.

Their lips parted but still he held her close. 'Oh, my dearest dear,' he murmured. 'My lovely girl—we seem to have wasted so much time.'

She stilled the regretful words with her hand on his lips. 'Never mind, darling. We'll have the rest of our lives together.'

He held her away to look down at her. 'You will marry me?'

'Now that I know you love me ... yes,' she assured him quietly.

'I love you,' he said emphatically. 'More than anything in the world—more than I ever thought possible.'

The room was enfolded in silence while they exchanged the joyous vows of mutual love and gloried in the first, enchanting moments of full and utter confidence in the love they shared.

Some hours later, when they had arranged their future to their satisfaction, Dominic said lightly as he sat with his arm about his lovely Helen: 'I can see that you need a tight rein, my darling. I didn't realise that you were prone to quixotic impulses ... if Janet hadn't saved my bacon this evening I would still be marrying her next week. And now I find that you're partly to blame ... that you've been pushing her to the altar for all you were worth!'

She smiled. 'I was determined that you

shouldn't be hurt again ... and I honestly believed that she was in love with you.'

'Perhaps she was ... a little. In the early days.' He hesitated. He would not tell Helen that Janet had confessed to being in love with someone else ... it was her secret. 'I feel a little guilty,' he went on ruefully. 'Janet seems to have had a rough deal in one way and another—I hope things work out for her eventually.'

She snuggled closer to him. 'Oh, I don't think you need to worry about Janet. Just before I came dashing round to offer a friendly shoulder for you to cry on, she was called to the telephone. Her feet didn't touch the stairs, I swear ... and all because she was told a Mr. Varndell was calling.' She chuckled softly. 'I think that's what made me see red ... that she should have thrown you over for a man she scarcely knows. I didn't know then, of course, that you were rubbing your hands with glee because she'd broken your engagement.'

'Varndell ...?'

'Oh, he's not important, darling,' she assured him and raised her face for a kiss. He needed no prompting and everything else was forgotten as their lips met once again....

Janet was breathless by the time she reached the telephone. Her heart was thumping painfully and so loudly that she stupidly wondered if he would hear it over the wire. She felt very stupid ... dazed and incredulous and almost sick with excitement.

'Hallo . . .'

He barely heard the whisper of her voice. 'Janet? That is Nurse Finlay?'

'Yes, it's me . . .' She clutched furiously at her composure. He would think her a silly schoolgirl. 'How are you, Eden?'

Her voice was cool and even more remote than the connection warranted. 'You recognised my voice, then?' A silly and obvious remark but he had never felt so tongue-tied in his life.

'Yes, of course. You were lucky to catch me . . . I've just come in,' she rattled on.

'I'm in London,' he said abruptly. 'I know it's rather late but could you meet me . . . for a drink?'

'Now?'

'Well . . . in ten minutes or so? I'll come and pick you up.' He knew he was pleading but he no longer cared.

'Well . . . yes, all right,' she said shyly.

'Good . . . ten minutes, then.'

Janet heard the click as he cradled the receiver and she stood staring at the wall for a long minute before she hurriedly replaced her own receiver.

His call had come out of the blue—and on a night when she had longed for him desperately. Was it possible that he had sensed her need of him? Could such things happen? Or was he merely at a loose end and had happened to think of her? Oh, what did it matter? Why question what the gods sent? She would see him again, hear his voice, bask in his smile, know the touch of his hand—what more could she want right now?

She flew back to her room to check her hair and face. Sally looked up in surprise as she darted from mirror to drawer to mirror to wardrobe. 'Going out again?'

'Yes . . . that was a—a friend. He wants me to meet him for a drink.' She was almost singing.

Sally glanced at her shrewdly. Was this man the explanation for that abruptly ended engagement to Dominic Hammond? The colour on Janet's cheeks, the stars in her eyes, the air of general radiance seemed to supply the answer and a faint smile touched her lips as she returned to her text-books.

'What happened to Helen?' Janet asked carelessly as she slipped into a coat and snatched a bright scarf from her drawer. She had been hurt and upset by Helen's scolding but all that was forgotten now. She did not even pause to wonder why Helen should be so anxious for her to marry Dominic . . .

'She dashed out without saying where she was going. Not far because she didn't bother to powder her nose—just picked up her cloak and hurried out.'

Janet moved towards the door with one last glance at her reflection in the mirror. 'We are mean,' she said lightly. 'You seem to spend so many evenings on your own.'

'Oh, I don't mind. Who could concentrate on study with you two giggling and chattering all evening, anyway?' she teased. 'I think I'm the only one of us who takes nursing seriously ... and I never even wanted to be a nurse in the first place! I know how it will be ... you and Helen will both give up your training to get married and I shall be the only one to get my badge.'

Janet suddenly darted to drop a light kiss on her hair. 'And you'll deserve it, ducky—believe me!' Then she was gone with wings on her heels, hurrying to the man she loved ...

Eden tossed away his half-smoked cigarette as she came through the gates. He leaned across to open the car door and she gave him a tremulous smile as she got in and sat beside him.

She was trembling and there was a wretched sickness at the pit of her stomach. She had never realised that love could be like this.

Then he covered her hand with his own for a brief moment—and the world steadied and she was calm and quiet again.

'Where are we going?'

'To a little pub on the other side of the river. It's quiet and friendly ... and we'll be able to talk in peace.'

As they drove across the bridge with the dark, treacly Thames flowing eternally on its way and the fairy lights burning along the

Embankment, they talked of London and its magic. Janet was content. She would have talked of anything if it pleased him—sufficient for her that she sat by his side and knew the balm of his presence, the ease for the heart that had ached for so long.

As he had promised, the pub was quiet and friendly—and they were soon ensconced at a corner table with their drinks.

'You must have thought it odd of me to telephone you at nine o'clock at night,' he said, smiling.

'Oh, no! I was too pleased that you hadn't phoned earlier when I was out,' she said frankly.

His eyes were warm as they rested on her candid, pretty face. Then they moved casually to the slim, sensitive hands that cradled her glass. Eagerness leaped to his eyes and he strove to keep that same eagerness from his voice as he said lightly, tapping her left hand: 'No ring.'

She coloured prettily. 'No.'

'No engagement?'

'Not any more. I ... I just couldn't marry him, after all.'

'Better to know now than later.'

'Yes ... that's what he said. He was—very kind, very understanding.' Abruptly she hid her hands beneath the table, clasping them in her lap. 'Did you finish your book, Eden?' She was slightly breathless.

He accepted the change of subject without comment. 'Not yet ... it's been giving me a great deal of trouble. I haven't really had my mind on it, I suppose.'

'Oh ... I'm sorry.'

He grinned. 'So are my publishers. They hoped to bring it out in the autumn.'

'I wish I could write ... it must be nice to please yourself whether you work or not.'

He looked at her, one eyebrow raised in amusement. 'Doesn't nursing appeal any more?'

'I don't know ... just lately everything seems to have gone wrong. I guess one has to be really dedicated to make a good nurse. I'm seriously thinking of giving it up and going back to Cumberland.'

He was struck by the note of sadness in her voice.

'Is that really what you want to do? Or are you just upset about your engagement?'

'Oh, that was a mistake, anyway,' she admitted with a shrug. 'I knew I couldn't ever marry Dominic.'

'Not your type?'

'Not really.' Suddenly she smiled at him. 'But you don't want a sob story, Eden. I'm all right, really—just a fit of the blues, I'm afraid. It's so nice to see you again ... I feel loads better already.'

'Cure for all ills—that's me!' he joked.

She put her hand on his arm impulsively.

'You are nice!'

'Shall we make it a mutual admiration society?' He leaned forward. 'I think you're nice, too, Janet—much too nice for my peace of mind. You don't have to listen to this—and you can wipe it off the slate if you wish—but the reason I can't write these days is because you're on my mind too much. When you told me you were getting married it hit me right between the eyes. I guess it sounds pretty naive, Janet—but I fell in love with you on that train and it's one of those diseases that are virtually incurable when it hits you as hard as it hit me. I never meant to say any of this ... I thought you might even be married by now. But tonight—I don't know, I was feeling pretty low and I wanted desperately to see you. Now—well, you're no longer engaged and that news has gone to my head. I'm talking too much, I know ... I'm embarrassing you and I'm sorry. But I wanted you to know how I feel ... and I want you to tell me if there's any chance at all that you might come to feel the same way in time. Will you let me see you—often? Will you give me a chance ... will you, Janet?'

She listened in silence, her mouth tremulous, her eyes suddenly bright with unshed tears. He was saying all the things she had wanted to hear and feared that she never would. He was offering her the happiness which had become all important to her since the day she had met him by chance on that train. He was telling her

196

that he loved her—and in a very few moments she would tell him quietly, tenderly, simply that she loved him, too. . . .

As Helen settled to sleep that night, happy and secure in the knowledge of a settled future with Dominic, she thought of all that had happened since she had decided to train at St. Cecilia's.

Sally and her troubled heart, her hankering for a man who had married someone else, the rekindling of old feelings and sudden disillusion and the realisation that she had wasted her emotions on a worthless Roger Gale. . . .

Janet and her supposed love for Dominic, the nine days wonder of her friendship with him, the development of that friendship to the point of marriage, her chance meeting with a stranger on a train to whom she had become engaged that very evening, surprising her friends with the radiant announcement, the jilting of Dominic almost at the last moment . . . and the astonishment of his relief.

Herself . . . and the fatal fascination of Adrian's spell, the dormant love for Dominic which she had never suspected, her determination to ensure a happiness that she firmly believed he sought . . . and the realisation that she had almost pushed both him and Janet into a marriage neither wanted—and now the peace of mind and the quiet happiness of knowing that Dominic loved her and that they would spend the rest of their lives together...

A morass of complications, indeed. They had been a fine tangle of nurses, she thought sleepily—but now the tangles had been unravelled and soon Sally would be the only one of the three eager student-nurses left to hold the lamp high...

We hope you have enjoyed this Large Print book. Other Chivers Press or Thorndike Press Large Print books are available at your library or directly from the publishers.

For more information about current and forthcoming titles, please call or write, without obligation, to:

Chivers Press Limited
Windsor Bridge Road
Bath BA2 3AX
England
Tel. (01225) 335336

OR

Thorndike Press
P.O. Box 159
Thorndike, Maine 04986
USA
Tel. (800) 223–2336

All our Large Print titles are designed for easy reading, and all our books are made to last.